1/2 HOUR HELPER

Puzzles and Activities for ESL Students

JOAN ROBERTA WHITE

Prentice Hall Canada Inc., Scarborough, Ontario

Canadian Cataloguing in Publication Data
White, Joan Roberta, 1943-
Half hour helper
Includes index.
ISBN 0-13-036039-2
1. English language — Textbooks for second language learners.*
I. Title.
PE1128.W482 1993   428.3'4   C93-093474-1

Prentice-Hall, Inc., Englewood Cliffs, New Jersey
Prentice-Hall International, Inc., London
Prentice-Hall of Australia, Pty., Ltd., Sydney
Prentice-Hall of India Pvt., Ltd., New Delhi
Prentice-Hall of Japan, Inc., Tokyo
Prentice-Hall of Southeast Asia (Pte.) Ltd., Singapore
Editora Prentice-Hall do Brasil Ltda., Rio de Janeiro
Prentice-Hall Hispanoamericana, S.A., Mexico

ISBN: 0-13-036039-2

Acquisitions Editor: Marjorie Munroe
Developmental Editor: Linda Gorman
Copy Editor: Mia London
Production Editor: Karen Frances Sacks
Production Coordinator: Anita Boyle
Design: Dianne MacKenzie and Olena Serbyn
Page Layout: Tanya Stricek
Illustrations: Don Gauthier

1 2 3 4 5   97 96 95 94 93

Printed and bound in Canada.

TABLE OF CONTENTS

PART A ~ TEACHER'S NOTES AND ANSWERS

PART B ~ STUDENT PUZZLES

TABLE OF CONTENTS

TABLE OF CONTENTS

How many times have you and your students had a great and productive day? You have completed everything you had planned and your students are still in the mood for more learning. You look at the clock and realize you have some time before the class ends. What can you do for twenty or thirty minutes to take advantage of the students' enthusiasm?

How often have you had a bad day? Nothing is going right. The students' attention wanders for any number of reasons. Your planned lessons are not getting the response you had hoped for.

How many times, in a community adult program or parent and preschool program, do your students arrive at different times? You cannot start instructing the class because not everyone has arrived.

Well, now you can reach for **Half Hour Helper**, a puzzle book that will solve your problem. The puzzles alone are the instant solution to filling these times. Moreover, the puzzles are also a source of additional teacher-directed activities. You can

- review spelling problems;

- evaluate comprehension of phonetic patterns;

- enlarge general vocabulary;

- learn and review information about Canada; and

- motivate short writing activities.

Half Hour Helper is divided into two sections: Part A, Teacher's Notes and Answers, and Part B, Student Puzzles.

The Teacher's Notes include directions for supplementary uses of the puzzles, including explanations of the headings, pre-activities, general directions, variations, additional activities and the answers to the puzzles.

PRE-ACTIVITY

Pre-activities are sometimes necessary to help students do the puzzles with minimal guidance from the teacher. They consist of one or more of the following:

- introduction or review of relevant vocabulary;

- working with "touchables" before doing a puzzle in the abstract; and

- doing one or two examples of the puzzle activity on the blackboard.

GENERAL DIRECTIONS

General directions are given for each activity. They are usually identical to the instructions given to the students on each puzzle page, but some additional information may be included for further guidance.

VARIATIONS

Variations on how to do some of the puzzles are suggested. Using the variations, some puzzle pages can be used more than once, or puzzles at the end of a unit can be done differently for variety.

ANSWERS

A list of answers is given for most puzzles. In some cases, there might be solutions not included in the possible answers. Accept any reasonable response the students give you.

ADDITIONAL ACTIVITIES

Additional activities follow the answers to some puzzles. These activities can be used immediately or at another time. Additional activities include grammar and spelling exercises, writing practice, research assignments, maps and map making, field trips, and discussions.

The Student Puzzles follow the Teacher's Notes and may be photocopied for classroom use.

SUGGESTED LEVELS FOR USE OF PUZZLES

Puzzle	Literacy	Beginner	Intermediate
Colour Puzzles	all	all	all
Odd One Out	1, 2	1, 2, 3	all
New One In		1, 2, 3	all
Categories	1, 3	1 - 9	all
Your Category Lists		all	all
Pick a Letter		all	all
Letter Puzzles		all	all
Rhyme Time	1, 2, 3	all	all
Crossword Puzzles	1, 2	1 - 6	all
Up and Down		1, 2, 3	all

Thank you to all the students whose enthusiasm encouraged me to create these puzzles.

Thank you to the other members of my teaching staff: Mary, Anne, Eleanor, Marguerite, and the two Janes, whose support is always appreciated.

Thank you to Natasha Diacyzk for the original art ideas.

Thank you to the reviewers for their helpful suggestions and constructive criticism of my original manuscript.

Thank you to the editors at Prentice-Hall who made the publication of my first book an exciting and rewarding experience.

Finally, thanks to my husband Dave, who introduced me to the wonders of our computer and word processing and so who inspired me to write this book.

Dedicated to all my ESL students — past, present and future

PART A

TEACHER'S NOTES AND ANSWERS

Level ~ Literacy/Beginner

PRE-ACTIVITY
Review colours and the names of the colours.

GENERAL DIRECTIONS

Explain that each puzzle examines a different colour. The answers are objects that are this colour or are associated with the colour in some way. For example, green means "*go*"; "red" means "*stop*" or "*it makes you think of something hot*". Students read the clue and write the answer in the box to the right of the clue. As well, students match some of the written clues with pictures at the bottom of the page.

Students can do the puzzles individually or with a partner. For literacy groups, do the puzzle as a class. Students take turns reading clues and together discover the answer.

Note: As an aid to literacy or with very basic classes, you could list the answer words on the blackboard in alphabetical order.

ADDITIONAL ACTIVITIES (FOR ALL THE PUZZLES)

1. Ask students to find objects around the classroom or to think of familiar things at home. Individually or in pairs, they can make up a colour clue for these objects and present them orally to the class. The others guess the identity of the item. Alternatively, each student could write a clue on a piece of paper and put them into a box or bag. Each student then draws a paper from the box, reads the clue, and suggests an answer.

2. Ask students to make up a sentence that shows they know the meaning of selected clue words.

3. Use some of the answer words to expand vocabulary by developing word families. Change the initial consonant to other consonants or consonant blends.
   Example:
   From the **red** puzzle ~ stop ~> cop, hop, mop, pop, top, chop, crop, shop
   From the **yellow** puzzle ~ sun ~> bun, fun, gun, nun, pun, run, stun, spun

ANSWERS

Red

1. ketchup   2. stop sign   3. maple leaf   4. apple   5. wine   6. heat/hot
7. tomato   8. chili pepper/cayenne

Orange

1. orange   2. leaf/leaves   3. fire/flames   4. carrot   5. pumpkin
6. cheese   7. tangerine/mandarin   8. orange juice

Yellow

1. sun   2. yolk   3. mustard   4. banana   5. lemon   6. grapefruit
7. gold   8. daffodil/dandelion

Green

1. grass   2. traffic light   3. grape   4. leaf   5. peas   6. bean
7. pepper   8. frog

Blue

1. sky   2. eyes   3. lake   4. jeans   5. bluejay   6. blueberry   7. ink
8. robin's egg

Purple

1. grape   2. eggplant   3. lilac   4. cabbage   5. violet/crocus   6. plum

Black

1. road/highway   2. crow   3. pepper   4. tire(s)   5. night   6. coffee
7. hair   8. oil

Brown

1. chocolate   2. flower pot/earth   3. eyes   4. cow   5. bread   6. hair
7. wood   8. peanut butter

White

1. cloud   2. snow   3. paper   4. socks   5. potato   6. salt   7. milk
8. sugar   9. polar bear   10. rice

Level ~ All levels if students are familiar with the vocabulary. The first puzzles are easier than the later ones.

PRE-ACTIVITY

Gather the students around a table.

1. Use "touchables". Randomly place four pieces of fruit and one vegetable on the table. Ask the students to choose which object does not belong. Ideally, someone will choose the vegetable.

   Teacher: "Why did you choose the potato?"
   Student: "It's a vegetable and all the others are fruits."

   Replace the fruits and vegetable with a knife, fork, spoon, serving spoon, and can opener. Repeat the exercise.

2. Replace the eating utensils with four objects of one colour and one of another colour. Repeat the exercise. The concept in this version is more abstract.

3. Randomly write the names of a teacher and four students on the blackboard. Ask the students which one is different. Circle the name.

   Explain that the "Odd One Out" puzzles are the same kind of activity with words. Read the directions of the first puzzle with the students. Always do the first line of each puzzle with the students.

   With literacy students, do the whole puzzle together. Ask individual students to read a line of words out loud and to choose the word that does not belong.

GENERAL DIRECTIONS

In each line of words, one word does not belong. The student circles that word and should be prepared to explain why it is different. In some cases, more than one answer is correct. A list of answers is provided, but accept any logical answer if the student can justify his or her choice.

ANSWERS

ODD ONE OUT 1

1. feet ~ They are not part of the head.
2. shirt ~ It is clothing for men and women.
3. meat ~ It is not a kitchen utensil.
4. fish ~ It is not a dairy product.

5. paper ~ You use the other objects to write on the paper.
6. pen ~ You use this item to write on the others.
7. sandwich ~ It is not a beverage.
8. crow ~ It is not a mammal.
9. coat ~ It is not worn on the foot.
10. egg ~ It is not a meal.

ADDITIONAL ACTIVITIES

A ~ Dictionary Skills

1. Choose the clothing words and put them in alphabetical order.
2. Choose the food words and put them in alphabetical order.

B ~ Grammar Skills

Pick out the words with double letters.

(feet, dress, glass, cheese, book, letter, coffee, boot, slipper, runner, supper, egg, dinner)

Ask the following questions:

1. How do you pronounce these words?
   As the students pronounce the words, put them in three different columns on the board: double vowels, final double consonant, and central double consonants.

2. How are they different?
   Try to elicit the number of syllables in each word. You can then demonstrate how a two-syllable word is divided between the double consonants.

3. What other words do you know with the same double vowel sounds?

C ~ Spelling Challenge

How many smaller words can you make from "breakfast" in line 10? Each word must have three or more letters. You can only use a letter the number of times it appears in "breakfast."

Do this exercise as a class activity. Demonstrate how to make rhyming words by changing the initial consonant or consonant blend. Show how nouns can be made plural or verbs changed by adding an "s."

Here is a partial list: break(s), steak(s), teak, beak, freak, fast, faster, are, bare, fare, stare, ear, bear, tear, fear, bar, far, tar, star, bake, brake, fake, rake, sake, take, bat, rat, fat, rate, skate, fate.

ODD ONE OUT 2

1. glove ~ You use the others to carry things.
2. tree ~ The others are precipitation or weather.
3. potato ~ It is a vegetable, not a fruit.
4. airplane ~ It is air, not ground, transportation.
5. school ~ People do not live in a school.
   tent ~ A tent is smaller than all the others.
6. sky ~ It is not green.
7. aunt ~ She is a female relative.
8. meat ~ The others are desserts.
9. Canada ~ It is a country. The others are capital cities.
10. students ~ Students are people, not inanimate objects.

ADDITIONAL ACTIVITIES

A ~ Dictionary Skills

1. Find the five words that have three syllables. (These words are apartment, grandfather, Ottawa, potato, Washington.)
2. Why are two words capitalized?
3. What words can be made plural? Spell them.

B ~ Spelling Challenge

How many smaller words can you make from "apartment" in line 5? Each word must have three or more letters. You can only use a letter the number of times it appears in the word. There are at least 30 words that you can make.

See Additional Activity C ~ Spelling Challenge in **Odd One Out 1** for hints on forming words.

ODD ONE OUT 3

1. spoon ~ You do not fry or cook things in it.
2. pear ~ It is a fruit not a vegetable.
3. dress ~ It is clothing only for a female. Or, the others are all outdoor clothing for cold weather.
4. bed ~ It is not kitchen furniture.
5. roof ~ This is an outside part of a house.
6. paper ~ You use the others to write something you can read whereas you use paper to write on.

7. friend ~ He or she is not part of an immediate family.
8. rain ~ It is not a description of temperature.
9. body ~ The others are diseases that affect the body.
10. Spain ~ English is not an official language.
    Australia ~ It is a continent as well as a country. Or, it is in the southern hemisphere.

ADDITIONAL ACTIVITIES

A ~ Categorizing

Pick out the four machines. Which is the newest machine? Which machines are almost the same?

B ~ Dictionary Skills

Pick out the nine words that start with "p." Put them in alphabetical order.

(pan, paper, pea, pear, pen, pencil, pot, potato, pox)

C ~ Spelling Challenge

1. Find words that rhyme.
   (Rhyming pairs are floor/door, mother/brother, rain/Spain, and hot/pot.)
2. What other words can you think of that rhyme with these words?

ODD ONE OUT 4

1. Mexico ~ It is not in South America.
   Brazil ~ Its official language is Portuguese not Spanish.
2. trumpet ~ The others are stringed instruments.
3. cauliflower ~ It is not a flower.
4. dishtowel ~ It is not found in the bathroom.
5. plate ~ It will not hold something to drink.
6. sock ~ You wear this on your foot, not on your body.
7. peas ~ The others are desserts.
8. mouse ~ The others are big animals.
   whale ~ It lives in water.
9. carrot ~ It is orange not red.
10. country ~ It is not water.

ADDITIONAL ACTIVITIES

A ~ Discussion Questions

1. Look at line 2. What are the names of some other instruments?
2. Does anyone in the class play an instrument? If yes, which one?
3. The trumpet is a brass instrument. What are some other brass instruments?

B ~ Quick Observations

1. Which is the five syllable word?
2. What are the five compound words in the puzzle?
3. What is the only plural word in the puzzle?
4. What is the biggest thing in the puzzle? What is the smallest?

C ~ Dictionary Skills

1. Find three words with a long "a" sound. Why is the "a" long?
2. How many words can you find with a short "a" sound?

D ~ Spelling Challenge

How many smaller words can you make from "cauliflower" in line 3? Each word must have three or more letters. You can only use a letter the number of times it appears in the word. There are at least 40 words you can find.

See Additional Activity C ~ Spelling Challenge in **Odd One Out 1** for hints on forming words.

ODD ONE OUT 5

1. flour ~ It does not add flavour to other foods.
2. grape ~ The others are citrus fruits.
3. ape ~ It walks on two feet, the others on four.
4. tomato ~ All the others grow in the earth.
5. squirrel ~ You do not usually eat squirrel meat. Or, farmers do not raise squirrels.
6. office ~ You will not usually find children in an office.
   house ~ This building is the only one in which people live.
7. grass ~ The others are very tall or very high. Or, grass is living.
8. flower ~ The others are green.
9. nose ~ You have only one nose.
10. chocolate ~ It's not naturally white.
    chalk ~ You cannot eat this substance.

ADDITIONAL ACTIVITIES

A ~ Quick Observations

1. Find the ten animals. Which animal is not native to Canada?
2. Find the two plural words.
3. Find the four compound words.

B ~ Dictionary Skills

1. Find the words that contain "ea" together. How do they sound different from each other?
2. What other words have a long "e" sound?
3. Find the three words that have the same "ou" sound. Can you think of more words that have this sound?

C ~ Spelling Challenge

How many smaller words can you make from "grapefruit" in line 2. Each word must have three or more letters. You can only use a letter the number of times it appears in the word. There are at least 35 words you can find.

See Additional Activity C ~ Spelling Challenge in **Odd One Out 1** for hints on forming words.

ODD ONE OUT 6

1. to ~ It is a preposition, not a verb.
2. I ~ It is a pronoun, not a preposition.
3. fast ~ It is an adverb and an adjective.
4. us ~ It is an objective pronoun, not a subjective pronoun.
5. house ~ It is the only singular noun.
6. song ~ It is a noun, not a verb form.
7. ran ~ It is an irregular past verb form.
8. teach ~ It is a verb, not a noun.
9. free ~ It is an adjective, not a noun.
10. liked ~ It is a verb that does not double its final letter before adding the suffix.

ADDITIONAL ACTIVITIES

A ~ Grammar and Spelling

1. What are the adjective forms of the adverbs in line 3?
2. What are the past forms of the verbs in line 1?

3. Make a chart to show the two forms of the pronouns (objective and subjective) in line 4.
4. Put the words in line 6 in alphabetical order.
5. Write the "ing" form of the verbs in line 7.
6. Make a sentence using as many words as you can from line 8.

B ~ Quick Test

Look at line 9. Use where you live to give a proper name for each noun.

ODD ONE OUT 7

1. woman ~ It is singular, not plural.
2. buses ~ It is plural, not singular, Or, it has two syllables, not one.
3. can ~ It is positive, not negative.
4. will ~ It is the future, not the past, tense.
5. play ~ It is the present, not the past, tense.
6. elephant ~ It is a noun, not an adjective.
7. doctor ~ It is not a compound word.
8. leg ~ It is singular, not plural. Or, it is the only word with a single "e."
9. stopped ~ It is a regular past tense; the others are irregular.
10. brown ~ It is an adjective, not a noun.

ADDITIONAL ACTIVITIES

A ~ Grammar and Spelling

1. What are the long forms of the contractions in line 3?
2. What are the root verbs of the past tenses in lines 4, 5, and 9?
3. Find the words with a long vowel sound. Write them on the blackboard in groups to show different rules: final silent "e," double vowels, and "other."

B ~ Word Game

Look at the compound words in line 7.

bus driver ~ What other words can you make with **bus**?
(bus lane, bus shelter, bus stop, school bus, tour bus)

homemaker ~ What other words can you make with **home**?
(homeland, homemade, home run, homesick, homeward, homework)

firefighter ~ What other words can you make with **fire**?
(firecracker, fire department, fire engine, fire escape, fire extinguisher, firefly, fire hydrant, fireplace, fireproof, fire station, firewood, fireworks)

Level ~ High Beginner to Intermediate if students are familiar with the vocabulary

PRE-ACTIVITY

Gather the students around a table.

1. Use "touchables." At one end of the table, spread the following objects: a piece of chalk, a notebook, a toy car, a ball, and a carrot. At the other end of the table, place a pen, pencil, magic marker, and crayon. Ask the students to choose which of the first group of objects belongs with the second group. Ideally, someone will choose the chalk.

   Teacher: "Why did you choose the chalk?"
   Student: "It's something to write with."
   "I can write with it."
   "It writes on something."
   "It writes."

   Return the chalk to the first group and replace the second set of objects with four vegetables. Again, ask students to choose the object from the first group that matches the new set. If necessary, repeat the exercise with a set of toys.

2. Do the same activity using pictures cut from magazines.

3. Explain that the puzzle set **New One In** uses only words. On the board, write out the words that match the objects from step one and redo the example using only the words.

GENERAL DIRECTIONS

The words in each group are associated in some way. From the words in the box at the bottom of the page, the student chooses the one that corresponds to each group. The student should be able to explain why he or she chose each word.

ANSWERS

NEW ONE IN 1

1. fish ~ pets
2. knees ~ parts of the body
3. cheeks ~ parts of the face

4. grandmother ~ people in the family
5. red ~ colours
6. counter ~ things in a kitchen
7. verb ~ parts of speech
8. snack ~ meals, things to eat
9. loony ~ coins
10. dress ~ clothes

NEW ONE IN 2

1. purple ~ colours
2. milk ~ beverages
3. bicycle ~ methods of transportation
4. eraser ~ things in a school or an office
5. sock ~ coverings for your feet
6. hand ~ body parts
7. Yellowknife ~ provincial and territorial capitals
8. she ~ pronouns
9. fog ~ aspects of weather
10. pig ~ farm animals

NEW ONE IN 3

1. baby ~ people
2. apartment ~ places to live; places to find shelter
3. pear ~ fruit
4. taxi ~ methods of transportation
5. chickadee ~ Canadian birds
6. freezing ~ temperatures
7. Ireland ~ countries in which English is an official language
8. dining room ~ rooms in a house
9. daisy ~ Canadian flowers
10. forehead ~ parts of the head

NEW ONE IN 4

1. grandmother ~ relatives; members of the family
2. note ~ things to read
3. can ~ containers to hold liquid
4. chalk ~ writing tools

5. electrician ~ occupations
6. teachers ~ parts of a school
7. ice cream ~ dairy products
8. pancakes ~ breakfast foods
9. yen ~ money
10. Quebec City ~ provincial capitals

NEW ONE IN 5

1. uncle ~ male members of a family
2. clarinet ~ musical instruments
3. niece ~ female members of a family
4. bat ~ animals that fly
5. seal ~ things that swim
6. bench ~ places to sit
7. sailboat ~ methods of water transportation
8. river ~ things that make you wet; things that have water
9. Spain ~ European countries
10. conversation ~ ways to communicate with other people

NEW ONE IN 6

1. onion ~ vegetables that grow and ripen in the ground
2. basketball ~ spherical objects
3. pineapple ~ fruits that do not grow in Canada
4. basil ~ herbs
5. wheat ~ edible grains
6. cabbage ~ vegetables that grow and ripen above the ground
7. apricot ~ fruits that grow in Canada
8. camel ~ edible meat
9. lid ~ round objects
10. cookies ~ desserts; foods eaten after the main course

Level ~ Please see the instructions for individual puzzles.

GENERAL DIRECTIONS

These puzzles can be done alone or with a partner. The words in the box at the top of the page belong under one of the headings. In some cases, words can go in more than one category. Accept any reasonable answer as long as the students can explain their decisions.

ANSWERS

The answers are self-evident for each puzzle.

CATEGORY 1 ~ FEELINGS

Level ~ Literacy/Beginner/Intermediate

ADDITIONAL ACTIVITIES

A ~ Discussion Questions

1. Have you ever had any of these feelings? When?
2. What makes you have these good and bad feelings?
3. What other feelings have you had?
4. What do you do when you feel …?
   The students might answer:
   When I'm happy, I smile. (I laugh. I call my mother. I sing. …)
   When I'm lonely, …
   When I'm angry, …
   and so on.

B ~ Writing

1. Write about a time when you had one of these feelings.
2. Draw a picture of yourself when you are happy. Talk to your classmates about it. Write a story about the picture.

C ~ Comprehension

Make up some events for your students like the following example:

Ana moved to Vancouver with her new husband Pedro. Her parents live far away in El Salvador. She didn't know they were saving their money to come to Canada too. One night she heard a knock on her apartment door. When she opened the door, she was saw her parents standing there in the hall. She felt ...

Ask your students what feelings the stories evoke in them.

D ~ Grammar and Spelling

1. Form comparatives and superlatives.
   a) Add "er" and "est" to the appropriate adjectives.
      (cold, brave, sad, happy, healthy, hungry, angry, sick, proud, lonely)
   b) Use "more" and "most" before the appropriate adjectives.
      (relaxed, nervous, tired, scared, surprised, embarrassed)

E ~ Observation

Spread pictures of people on a table. Hand out flashcards of "feeling" words. Ask students to match the cards to the pictures. You can use comparatives and superlatives here as well, if you have pictures to match.

F ~ Research

Give old magazines to the students. Ask them to find pictures of people showing many different feelings, and to cut the pictures out and label them. Put these pictures on the wall or bulletin board and review them with the class. Eliminate duplications and keep a displayed set for future reference.

CATEGORY 2 ~ FOOD

Level ~ Beginner/Intermediate

ADDITIONAL ACTIVITIES

A ~ Discussion Questions

1. Which foods from the puzzle do you usually eat at your home?
2. Which foods have you never eaten?
3. What is your favourite food or drink from each column?
   "I like ..."
   "I love ..."

4. What foods are your least favourite?
   "I don't like ..."
   "I can't stand ..."
   "I hate ..."
5. Give two other foods you eat for meals and snacks and two other drinks you enjoy.

B ~ Writing

A Dream Dinner ~ If you could have any meal cooked for you and served to you, what would it be?

C ~ Research

1. Distribute grocery flyers or magazines and ask your students to find examples of the foods mentioned. Label the pictures and display them on a bulletin board or chart paper.
2. Use flyers from different supermarkets, if available, and ask students to compare prices. Which store has the "best buy?"

CATEGORY 3 ~ ROOMS OF THE HOUSE

Level ~ Literacy/Beginner

ADDITIONAL ACTIVITIES

A ~ Discussion Questions

1. What other objects can you find in these three rooms?
2. Describe each of the rooms in your home. Use the words from your lists.

B ~ Writing

1. Describe your kitchen, your living room, and your bedroom. Use the words from your lists.
2. Divide the class into small groups. Then give the students the following instructions: Draw a floor plan of one of these rooms in your home. Describe the room to your group. (The teacher should do an example first.)

C ~ Grammar and Spelling

How many small words can you make from "refrigerator?" Each word must have three or more letters. You can only use a letter the number of times it appears in "refrigerator."

CATEGORY 4 ~ CANADIAN ANIMALS

Level ~ Beginner/Intermediate

ADDITIONAL ACTIVITIES

A ~ Observation

Display coloured pictures of as many of these Canadian animals as possible. Make a flashcard for each picture. Either match word cards with pictures or do this activity orally.

B ~ Comprehension

1. Animals can be further divided into more specific categories. Separate these animals into mammals, birds, insects, reptiles, and amphibians. Remember ~ the whale is a mammal.
2. Be ready to explain some of the unusual answers in these exercises:
    polar bear in water ~ Polar bears eat fish and seals and so must swim to catch their food. They are very good swimmers.

    robin on the ground ~ The robin spends a lot of time on the ground searching for worms, its favourite food.

C ~ Discussion Questions

1. Which of these animals have you seen?
2. Which of these animals live in our province?
3. Where in Canada do the others live?
4. Which of these animals can be pets? Describe any pets you have had or have now.

D ~ Writing

Write a story with one of the following titles: "My Pet," "A Pet I Would Like to Have," "My Favourite Animal."

E ~ Research Project

Assign each student or pair of students one animal. That student or pair will find information, write a report, and orally tell the class about the animal. Students can use the school or local library, or the teacher can provide books.

F ~ Field Trip

Visit a local museum or zoo to see some of these animals.

G ~ Audio-Visual Aids

Show an educational video, if available, on some Canadian animals that are of particular interest to the students.

CATEGORY 5 ~ COUNTRIES AND CITIES

Level ~ Beginner/Intermediate

ADDITIONAL ACTIVITIES

A ~ Discussion Questions

1. Where in the world is Calgary? Is it a capital city?
   (Repeat this exercise for each city.)
2. Where in the world is Brazil? What language is spoken there? Is anyone in the class from Brazil? Do you know anyone from Brazil? (Repeat this exercise for each country.)

B ~ Map Work for Canada

1. What cities are in Canada? Find them on a large wall map of Canada.
2. How many other Canadian cities do you know? What Canadian cities have you visited? Make copies of the Canadian map from the Appendix. Find and locate the cities on the list.

C ~ Map Work for the World

1. Find the countries on a large world map. Does anyone in the class come from one of these countries?
2. Where are the cities that are not in Canada? Does anyone in the class come from one of these cities?
3. On the blackboard or chart paper, put the headings **Cities** and **Countries**. List the cities and countries the students come from. Add the cities and countries each student has visited. Students can show the rest of the class their countries and cities on the world map. (Be aware that some students may need help reading a map. Use it as an opportunity to do a lesson on map reading.)
4. Make copies of the outline map of the world from the Appendix. Find and label the countries from which your students emigrated.

CATEGORY 6 ~ MALE AND FEMALE

Level ~ Beginner/Intermediate

ADDITIONAL ACTIVITIES

A ~ Discussion Questions

1. Which words are on both lists?
2. Are men nurses in your country? Have you ever seen a male nurse?
3. Are women doctors in your country? Have you ever seen a female doctor?
4. How many male and female teachers have you had? Who was your favourite? Why?
5. Have you seen a male secretary? Who was his boss?
6. Ask these riddles out loud: When is a son not a male relative? (When it's a **sun**.)
7. When is an aunt not a female relative? (When it's an **ant**.)

B ~ Grammar and Spelling

What is the plural of wife? secretary? baby?

C ~ Game

Play How Many? (a circle game)

In this activity, the teacher and the students sit in a circle. The teacher starts by asking one student a question that begins with "How many…". That student answers, then asks another student in the circle the same question or another one. Continue until students are asking and answering around the circle very quickly. Sometimes a humorous question will be asked, and everyone will have a good laugh!

Teacher: "Amal, how many sisters do you have?"
Amal: "I have two. Juanita, how many babies do you have?"
Juanita: "One. Kuo Ying, how many brothers do you have?"
Kuo Ying: "I have two. Mohamad, how many grandmothers do you have?"
Mohamad: "One. Michiru, how many husbands do you have?"
Michiru: "Oh, just one! Pedro, how many husbands do you have?"…

CATEGORY 7 ~ THE SENSES

Level ~ High Intermediate

ADDITIONAL ACTIVITIES

A ~ Discussion Questions

1. How can you see good news?
2. What does sea water look like?
3. What does fire sound like?
4. What music do you like to hear?
5. What do you listen to on the radio?
6. Describe the smell of chocolate.
7. Talk about the smell of garlic.
8. What is your favourite taste?
9. How does music make you feel?
10. How does a wet dog feel?

Create your own questions or ask students to make up questions.

The feelings in this exercise are physical feelings. We also have emotional feelings. What are some emotional feelings? (See **Category 1 ~ Feelings**.)

B ~ Writing

Many opportunities present themselves in this puzzle for writing assignments. Some suggestions that relate to physical or emotional feelings follow. You can present your own ideas as well; students might also have suggestions.

"My Good News"
"The Most Beautiful Sight I Remember"
"That Smells Good!"
"That Smells Terrible!"
"The Best/Worst Thing I Have Ever Tasted"
"Lucky Me"
"A Happy Time in my Life"

CATEGORY 8 ~ NOUNS AND VERBS

Level ~ Beginner/Intermediate

ADDITIONAL ACTIVITIES

A ~ Grammar and Spelling

1. What are the meanings of the words that appear in both columns (watch, cut, work, walk)? Make up sentences to show their meanings.
2. What is the past tense of each verb?
3. Dictate words from the list and then change the vowel sound: cat, cot, cut; lake, like, Luke; letter, latter, litter; sing, song, sang, sung; come, came; write, wrote.

CATEGORY 9 ~ SINGULAR AND PLURAL

Level ~ Beginner/Intermediate

ADDITIONAL ACTIVITIES

A ~ Grammar and Spelling

1. Match any singular with its plural.
2. What is the plural of bus? lesson? pen?
3. What is the singular of geese? glasses? people?
4. Make compound words using **man**.
   a) Combine it with police, fire, sales, crew, space, and chair.
   b) Now combine it with hole, power, hunt, and kind.
5. Can you make the **man** plural in all of these words? Why not?
6. Can you make new words using **woman** in the place of **man**?
7. What are some words that refer to both men and women?
   (police officer, firefighter, salesperson, chairperson, crew member, astronaut, humanity, humankind)?

CATEGORY 10 ~ SINCE... FOR...

Level ~ Intermediate

ADDITIONAL ACTIVITIES

A ~ Discussion Questions

1. What have you done **since** Tuesday night?
   What have you done **since** you left your country?
   What will you do **for** the rest of the year?
   Where will you go **for** the summer holiday?
   and so on.
2. Ask students to make up sentences for some of the phrases, especially those that are used with both "**for**..." and "**since**...".

B ~ Grammar Comprehension

1. Make up a **cloze** exercise using the students' examples of "for..." and "since..." phrases. Leave a blank for "since" and "for." Make copies and pass the papers out as a comprehension exercise.
2. What phrases from the list can be used with other prepositions (on, after, by, at)?

Level ~ Intermediate

GENERAL DIRECTIONS

The students follow the directions in the box at the top of the page and write five words for each category.

The first four puzzles are general information puzzles and the last is a grammar puzzle. You can invent puzzles to challenge your own students.

ANSWERS

Your students will have many different answers. Share the results with the class. It will be interesting to see the variety of responses your students give.

Variations

1. Students can work individually.
2. Arrange students in pairs or small groups. Put a time limit on the exercise and, at the end of that period, compare lists.

Level ~ Beginner/Intermediate

PRE-ACTIVITY

1. Put the following letters and partial words on the blackboard.
   Draw a short blank before each partial word.

   A   B   C   G   L   O   P   S

__ range	__ emon
__ pple	__ herry
__ anana	__ trawberry
__ ear	__ rape

   Challenge the students to choose a letter from the top row to put in front of each group of letters to make a word. A letter can only be used once and all letters must be used. Students will find it quite easy to see the familiar patterns and complete this puzzle. Ask the students for a good name for the puzzle, for example "Fruits" or "Kinds of Fruit."

2. Do a second more challenging puzzle on the blackboard.

   B   C   D   G   H   J   M   P   S   T

__ at	__ acket
__ oat	__ ants
__ ittens	__ kirt
__ loves	__ ress
__ oots	__ ie

   a) Again, challenge the students to put a letter in front of each group to make a word. They will find that they can make many words.

   b) Put a restriction on the puzzle. The students must use all the letters and they can use each letter only once. This rule makes the puzzle more difficult. Do the exercise on the blackboard with the whole class.

   c) Students will find the correct solution by trying all possibilities and then, through the process of elimination, determining the correct answer. Write all possible initial letters in front of the word endings. Using coloured chalk for this part will make the choices clearer.

You should have the following list on the blackboard:

bchmps / at	jp / acket
bcg / oat	p / ants
m / ittens	s / kirt
g / loves	dp / ress
b / oots	dpt / ie

Explanation

1. Because only one letter will complete some words, that letter is, of course, the correct answer. Circle the initial letter in these words.

2. Because "g" is the only letter in front of "loves," making "gloves," it cannot be used anywhere else. Erase the "g" in front of "oat."

3. The "s" is used to make "skirt," so rub it out in front of "at."

4. The "p" is the only letter in front of "ants," making "pants." Erase it from the other places it appears.

5. The "b" is used to make "boots." Rub it out in the other places it appears.

6. Now, "c" is left for "coat." Rub it out in front of "at."

7. Continue with this process until you have the following list:

hat	coat
mittens	gloves
boots	jacket
pants	skirt
dress	tie

The first puzzles are easy; the answers are obvious. In later puzzles, students will have to play with the initial consonants as they did in the second example. But when they are ready, they will be able to complete these activities.

GENERAL DIRECTIONS

These activities are a collection of mixed alphabet puzzles. From a selection of letters at the top of the page, students choose a letter to be the initial sound for words in the chart. Each letter may be used only once. These puzzles, which are in categories, may be used as an additional activity to themes presented in class, to introduce a topic, or to review vocabulary. Or they can be used just for fun.

The puzzles are not named ~ providing a name for the puzzle is part of the puzzle!

ANSWERS

To correct puzzles, if there are problems, copy the puzzle page onto the blackboard, or make an overhead projection, and proceed as in the Pre-Activities.

PICK A LETTER 1

Newfoundland	Saskatchewan
Canada	Alberta
Ontario	Toronto
Quebec	Vancouver
Halifax	Manitoba
Yukon	Edmonton

What is a good name for this puzzle? Places in Canada, Canadian Places

ADDITIONAL ACTIVITIES

A ~ Discussion Questions

1. How many provinces are named in this puzzle?
2. What provinces are missing?
3. What cities are named?
4. What provinces are the cities in?
5. What city do you live in?
6. What province do you live in?
7. Which two answers are neither a province nor a city?

B ~ Map Work

1. Name all provinces and territories and their capitals.
2. Locate the provinces and capitals on a map of Canada. (Make copies of the map of Canada in the Appendix.)

C ~ Research (for High Intermediate Level students)

Have students work in pairs to do some research using books you have chosen. Each pair chooses one province (or territory) and prepares a simple presentation using the following guidelines: province, capital city, population, industries, basic geography, and agriculture.

PICK A LETTER 2

horse	porcupine
goat	lion
cow	moose
raccoon	squirrel
dog	elephant
beaver	fox

What is a good name for this puzzle? Animals, Mammals

ADDITIONAL ACTIVITIES

A ~ Observation

1. Display pictures of the animals and prepare flashcards with their names. The students match the pictures to the words.
   You can add other animals to those found in this list.
2. Put the pictures in animal size order, from smallest to largest.

B ~ Discussion Questions

1. Which two mammals are not native to Canada?
2. Which animals live in your country? Are they like the ones we have in Canada? Describe them.
3. Did you ever have one of these animals as a pet? on a farm?
4. Which animal is the biggest?
5. Which animal is the smallest?

C ~ Rhyming Challenge

Find groups of rhyming words for **cow**, **fox**, **dog**, and **moose**.

D ~ Field Trip

Visit a local museum or zoo to see mammals of Canada or, in particular, those native to your own area.

F ~ Research (for Intermediate Level students)

Have students work in pairs to do some research using books you have chosen. Students choose an animal and prepare a simple presentation using the following guidelines: physical appearance, habitat, food, and something special about this animal.

PICK A LETTER 3

robin	sparrow
pigeon	woodpecker
jay	owl
crow	duck
hawk	gull
eagle	blackbird

What is a good name for this puzzle? Canadian Birds, Birds of Canada

ADDITIONAL ACTIVITIES

A ~ Discussion Questions

1. What birds can you see in this area?
2. Do you have any of these birds in your country? How do you say their names in your language?
3. Which bird flies mostly at night?
4. What other Canadian birds do you know?

B ~ Observation

1. Put the bird names on flashcards and display pictures of the birds. Match the pictures and flashcards.
2. Use the picture cards to put the birds in order by size (smallest to largest).

C ~ Field Trip

Visit a local museum or zoo to see birds of Canada or, in particular, those native to your own area.

D ~ Research (for Intermediate Level students)

Have students work in pairs to do some research using books you have chosen. Students choose a bird and prepare a simple presentation using the following guidelines: physical appearance, habitat, food, and something special about this bird.

PICK A LETTER 4

teacher	eraser
ruler	walls
lessons	map
friends	pen
books	chair
desk	student

What is a good name for this puzzle? In the classroom, The Schoolroom, At School

ADDITIONAL ACTIVITIES

A ~ Alphabet Soup

What other objects can you find in the classroom that begin with these letters?

B ~ Grammar

Do a preposition exercise for each word on the list.

Teacher: "Where is your ruler?"
Student A: "It's in my pencil case."
Teacher: "Where is the map?"
Student B: "It's on the wall."

C ~ Counting

Teacher: "How many chairs are in this row? this group?"
Teacher: "How many friends do you have?"
Teacher: "How many pens are on your desk?"

D ~ Sequencing

You can do these steps one following the other or on different days, depending on your time limits and the abilities of your students.

1. Take the class outside and stand on the sidewalk facing the school. Using the **simple present** or **present continuous**, walk the students back to the classroom. Individual students take turns saying aloud what they are doing.

   Teacher: "What are you doing?"
   Student: "I am walking up the front walk."
   Teacher: "Now, what are you doing?"
   Student: "I walk up three steps."
   Student: "I open the door."

Student: "I go in the school."
Student: "I am passing the office."
Student: "I am passing the coat room."
Student: "I turn right…."

2. Once the students are seated, ask them to review how they returned to the classroom, using the past tense. Write their responses on the blackboard or on experience-chart paper.

   a) Blackboard Story

      i) Students can practise reading the story individually or as a group.

      ii) Erase the verbs. Students can read the story again, supplying the missing verbs. Erase the prepositions. Students can read the story again, supplying the missing prepositions.

   b) Experience Chart
   Experience charts give beginning students the opportunity to practise reading the story several times. Underline verbs in red. Circle prepositions in blue. Put a green box around nouns. Do some grammar drills with these marked words.

E ~ Map Making

Make a floor plan of the classroom.

F ~ Comparisons

Compare classrooms in Canada to classrooms in the students' home countries.

PICK A LETTER 5

room	kitchen
bedroom	hall
closet	door
floor	walls
attic	stairs
lights	gas

What is a good name for this puzzle? Parts of a House Inside, Inside a House

ADDITIONAL ACTIVITIES

A ~ Alphabet Soup

What other objects in the house can you think of that begin with each letter?

B ~ Counting

How many rooms (bedrooms, closets, doors) do you have in your home?

C ~ Map Making

Draw a simple floor plan of your home, showing the entrance, main hall and rooms, and the location of basic appliances and furniture. Then walk the students through your home.

Ask the students to draw simple floor plans of their homes. Each can then walk their classmates through it.

PICK A LETTER 6

roof	door
window	grass
yard	fence
tree	plants
birds	lawn
steps	children

What is a good name for this puzzle? Outside Parts of a House, Outside a House

ADDITIONAL ACTIVITIES

A ~ Discussion Questions

1. Using each letter, what other things can you think of outside a house?
2. Do you have a yard?
3. What kinds of plants do you have in your yard?
4. What kinds of trees do you have in your yard?

B ~ Map Making

Draw a simple map of your yard, showing the grass, garden, trees, bushes, play area for children, and so on. Talk about your yard. Then ask the students to draw maps of their yards following your example.

PICK A LETTER 7

dishes	sink
oven	cupboard
pot	microwave
knife	table
window	fork
bowl	light

What is a good name for this puzzle? The Kitchen, In the Kitchen

ADDITIONAL ACTIVITIES

A ~ Discussion Questions

1. Using each letter, what other things can you think of inside a house?
2. What things can you put on the table?
3. What things can you put in the oven?
4. What things can you put in the cupboard?

B ~ Rhyming Challenge

Arrange students in pairs. Each pair will find words to rhyme with "pot", "sink," and "light." Set a time limit.

PICK A LETTER 8

farmer	homemaker
nurse	secretary
mechanic	lawyer
cook	writer
doctor	bus driver
teacher	pharmacist

What is a good name for this puzzle? Occupations, Jobs People Have

ADDITIONAL ACTIVITIES

A ~ Discussion

1. What other occupations or jobs do you know of?
2. Can both men and women do these jobs?
3. Do you know someone who holds one of these occupations?

B ~ Observation

Prepare several flashcards and matching pictures of occupations. Spread the pictures on the table and hand out the cards. Have students match the cards to the pictures.

Variation ~ Write the occupations on two sets of differently coloured cards. Divide the class into two teams. Hand out the cards using one colour for each team. On a signal, the students will put the cards face down on the matching pictures. When one team is finished, the game stops. Turn the cards over to check if they match. One point is scored for each correct answer.

C ~ Writing

1. Write a story about your job in your country.
2. Write a story about what you want to do in Canada.

Level ~ High Beginners/Intermediate

PRE-ACTIVITY

To introduce this puzzle, challenge the students with the following question:

Teacher: "What is the first letter of the alphabet?"

Student: "A."

Teacher: "Give me a word that starts with "a" for these clues:

1. a crispy fruit,
2. the opposite of "before",
3. a large continent that touches the Atlantic Ocean,
4. a (pretty/handsome) student in our class [if you have a student whose name starts with "A"]."

Students give their answers orally. Ask a student to write the answer on the blackboard. Do not correct spelling mistakes. Ideally, other students will notice any errors.

GENERAL DIRECTIONS

There is a puzzle page for each letter of the alphabet except Xx, Yy, and Zz, which have been combined. Students read the definition and write the answer in the box to the right. Dictionaries may be used.

To correct the papers, write the numbers 1 to 12 on the blackboard in a set pattern you will use every time you present these puzzles. Assign different students to write the answers on the blackboard. Do not correct the answers or spelling at this time. When the students have finished writing their answers, take up each answer orally. Ask a student to read the clue. Ask if all students agree with the answer on the board and its spelling. This activity will encourage discussion and spelling corrections by the class.

Variations

1. Students work alone with or without a dictionary.
2. Each student works with a partner but does not use a dictionary. Students should work with various partners on different days so that students with different ability levels are paired. Mix strong students with weaker ones. Set a time limit depending on the students' capabilities. When the time is up, proceed as instructed in the General Directions.

3. *Focus on Listening* ~ Students work with partners. Student A has the puzzle and reads each clue to his or her partner, Student B, who must give the answer. Student A can help Student B by giving more information to help him or her get the answer but cannot show the puzzle to Student B. Student A will write the answer in the box on the puzzle page. To correct the work, proceed as instructed in the General Directions.

ADDITIONAL ACTIVITIES

These activities can be used with all of the alphabet puzzles.

1. Use the words in each puzzle to teach alphabetical order. This will help the students learn dictionary skills by forcing them to look at the second or even third letter of the words to alphabetize them.

2. Ask the students to write sentences using at least two of the words per sentence. Some students enjoy writing silly sentences in order to include as many words in the list as possible.

3. Have students work in pairs to write definitions of a new list of words. These words can be a review of the current theme lessons or miscellaneous words chosen by the students. Make copies of these puzzles for the class.

4. Use words from the list for grammar practice.
   a) Form other words from the same root. For example, if the noun form of the word is used in the puzzle, ask for the verb, adjective, and adverb forms.
   b) Form compound words from the words in the puzzles.
   c) Make the plural or singular of an answer word.
   d) Practise adding endings to the answer words, especially if they are irregular.

ANSWERS

Note: When judging the answers, accept any reasonable response if it begins with the correct letter. For a High Intermediate group, be quite critical about the answer agreeing with the clue. For example, if the clue asks for the plural, make sure the answer corresponds. This practice will make your students more self-aware when doing the puzzles.

A A A A A

1. apple   2. Alberta   3. Africa   4. actor   5. address   6. ankle
7. apron   8. afternoon   9. airport   10. atlas   11. ant   12. arm

B B B B B

1. bus   2. band-aid/bandage   3. beaver   4. British Columbia   5. blouse
6. boots   7. blue   8. ball   9. bird   10. baker   11. banana
12. butterfly/bee

C C C C C

1. Canadian   2. cold   3. clock   4. coat   5. cow   6. canary   7. canoe
8. clouds   9. core   10. Canada   11. cup   12. close/closed

D D D D D

1. doctor   2. December   3. dog   4. dentist   5. Delicious   6. day
7. desert   8. dollar(s)   9. door   10. dance   11. dessert   12. down

E E E E E

1. ears   2. early   3. exit   4. east   5. egg   6. eighty   7. eyes
8. end/ending   9. Earth   10. Edmonton   11. elbow   12. eraser

F F F F F

1. five   2. fall   3. fingers   4. fish/frog   5. face   6. floor   7. front
8. family   9. flowers   10. food   11. father   12. friend

G G G G G

1. grapefruit   2. green   3. garage   4. grasshopper   5. grandparents
6. gas/gasoline   7. glass   8. gorilla   9. gold   10. girl   11. glasses
12. grass

H H H H H

1. hip(s)   2. head   3. holiday   4. hot   5. hill   6. Halifax   7. hat/hood/hair
8. husband   9. hay   10. hand   11. honey   12. high school

I I I I I

1. ice   2. in   3. isn't   4. Indians/Inuit   5. itch(y)   6. insects   7. island
8. iron   9. it's   10. ink   11. important   12. ill

J J J J J

1. job   2. jewellery   3. John/James/Jim   4. Japan   5. jacket   6. jet
7. January   8. juice   9. June   10. janitor   11. jeans   12. jar

K K K K

1. ketchup 2. king 3. kick 4. key 5. kindergarten 6. knee
7. kitchen 8. kid 9. kept 10. Koran 11. kitten 12. kite

L L L L

1. leg(s) 2. last 3. lamb 4. lemon 5. library 6. ladder 7. lakes
8. left 9. letter 10. lung(s) 11. love 12. lunch

M M M M

1. Manitoba 2. money 3. milk 4. moustache 5. mother 6. mouse
7. Monday 8. moon 9. maple 10. mouth 11. mountains
12. mosquito

N N N N

1. nose 2. ninety-nine 3. Newfoundland 4. nest 5. nurse 6. noon
7. nickel 8. niece 9. north 10. neck 11. new 12. night

O O O O

1. orange 2. Ottawa 3. off 4. owl 5. old 6. October 7. over
8. office 9. oven 10. occupation 11. Ontario 12. out

P P P P

1. pepper 2. panda 3. pumpkin 4. parrot 5. pillow
6. Pacific (Ocean) 7. pizza 8. plumber 9. parents 10. provinces
11. pen/pencil 12. paw

Q Q Q Q

1. Quebec 2. question 3. queen 4. quit 5. quilt 6. quick
7. quack 8. quarter 9. quiet 10. question mark 11. quarterback
12. Quebec City

R R R R

1. robin 2. Regina 3. ruler 4. rattle 5. rug 6. restaurant
7. Rocky Mountains/Rockies 8. raincoat 9. rings 10. raisins
11. rose 12. radish/red pepper

S S S S

1. swim 2. socks/shoes 3. sun 4. south 5. skunk 6. supermarket
7. summer 8. saw 9. Saskatchewan 10. son 11. salt 12. skating/skiing

T T T T T

1. teeth   2. teacher   3. tulip   4. towel   5. twelve   6. train   7. Toronto
8. temperature   9. telephone   10. take   11. tea   12. Tuesday

U U U U U

1. under   2. uncle   3. us   4. underwear   5. up   6. undress   7. ugly
8. used   9. untidy   10. United States/U.S.A.   11. untrue   12. unhappy

V V V V V

1. vowels   2. vest   3. Valentine's Day   4. Vancouver   5. vegetables
6. violet   7. vacuum cleaner   8. verbs   9. Victoria   10. village
11. vase   12. VCR (video cassette recorder)

W W W W W

1. wool   2. waiter/waitress   3. Whitehorse   4. wall   5. wet   6. watch
7. Winnipeg   8. woman   9. waist   10. west   11. wheat   12. wing

X Y Z

1. zucchini   2. Yukon   3. yellow   4. x-ray   5. zebra   6. you're
7. Yellowknife   8. yen   9. zero   10. you   11. yes   12. yesterday

Level ~ Puzzles 1, 2, and 3: Literacy and Beginner
    Puzzles 4, 5, and 6: Intermediate

PRE-ACTIVITY

Write some simple words on the blackboard.

cat / fun / man / day / nine / all

Ask the students for words that rhyme with these words. Ask the students to suggest other rhyming pairs. Be sure to point out any suggestions that sound the same but are spelled differently.

GENERAL DIRECTIONS

Give these directions for Puzzles 1, 2, and 3:

1. Find the words in the box that rhyme and write them down in pairs. Be careful! Most of the words in the puzzle that rhyme have the same ending. **However**, some word endings in each puzzle sound the same but are spelled differently.

2. Read each sentence and fill in the blanks with rhyming words. Use the pictures to the right of the sentences to help you.

Give these directions for Puzzles 4, 5, and 6:

These puzzles are more difficult because there are no pictures to give clues. Students can read the directions themselves with the teacher adding explanations if necessary.

1. Find the words that rhyme in the box at the bottom of the page and write them down together.

2. Read each sentence. Choose rhyming words to put in the blanks so that the sentence makes sense.

Variations

1. Students can work alone.
2. Students can work with a partner, reading the sentences aloud to help verify the correct answers.

ANSWERS

RHYME TIME 1

1. A hat on a cat.
2. Jill went up the hill.
3. Wine for nine.
4. A star on a car.
5. The bell fell.
6. He stands on his hands.
7. Throw the ball at the wall.
8. Paul is tall.

RHYME TIME 2

1. Please lock the clock.
2. She picks up the sticks.
3. The man ran to the van.
4. Tea for me.
5. Ted is in bed.
6. Here are ten men.
7. Bob has a job.
8. The frog is on the log.

RHYME TIME 3

1. There's the door to the store.
2. Dick is sick.
3. That wine is mine.
4. Who has my shoe?
5. Pour more milk please.
6. Have fun in the sun.
7. A doll and a ball by the wall.
8. A house for a mouse.

RHYME TIME 4

1. My pet got wet in the rain.
2. My mother knits some mitts.
3. Jack has a backpack.
4. The coffee and tea were free.
5. Pina picks up six sticks.
6. She ate eight cookies.
7. He wrote a note about his boat.

RHYME TIME 5

1. Wayne has a cane.
2. Joan is talking on the phone.
3. I like to fly high in the sky.
4. Jane ran to the plane in the rain.
5. Joe shovelled the snow.
6. I hate to be late for a date.
7. Why did you buy the pie?

RHYME TIME 6

1. If I see a bear, it will scare me.
2. He told me it was cold.
3. Let's take a walk around the block.
4. Wait at gate eight at the airport.
5. The skin on my chin is thin.
6. There's a hole in the bowl.
7. The snow will blow all day.

Level ~ Beginner to Intermediate

Puzzles can be used to review a unit of work or just for enjoyment.

GENERAL DIRECTIONS

The crossword puzzles in this section are self-explanatory.

Each puzzle is set up on two pages.

The first two puzzles are very easy. The clues are pictures. Students write the word beside the picture and then transfer each word into the puzzle.

The remaining crosswords are a mixture of general knowledge puzzles and grammar puzzles.

Variations

1. Students work on the puzzles individually.
2. Arrange the students in pairs. One partner has the puzzle while the other has the clues with the list of answer words. The pair works together to solve the puzzle. They can help each other orally but cannot look at each other's page. The person with the clue page cannot give the answer but can give a further explanation or clue to help the partner doing the puzzle.

   Present the following vocabulary to ask for clarification:

   "Could you repeat that please?"
   "I'm sorry, I didn't understand. What did you say?"
   "Is that spelled … ?"
   "No, that won't fit. What was number (4) across again?"
   "I don't know. What is the next clue?"

ANSWERS
FRUITS AND VEGETABLES

ANSWERS
PARTS OF THE HEAD

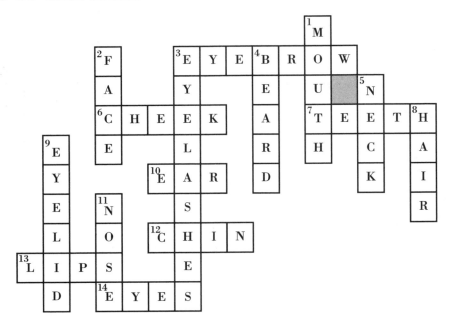

ANSWERS
PARTS OF THE BODY

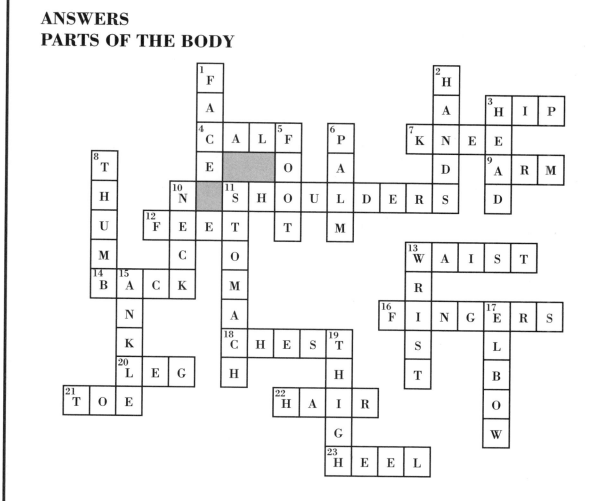

ANSWERS
PARTS OF THE HOUSE

ANSWERS
AT SCHOOL

**ANSWERS
CANADIAN MAP**

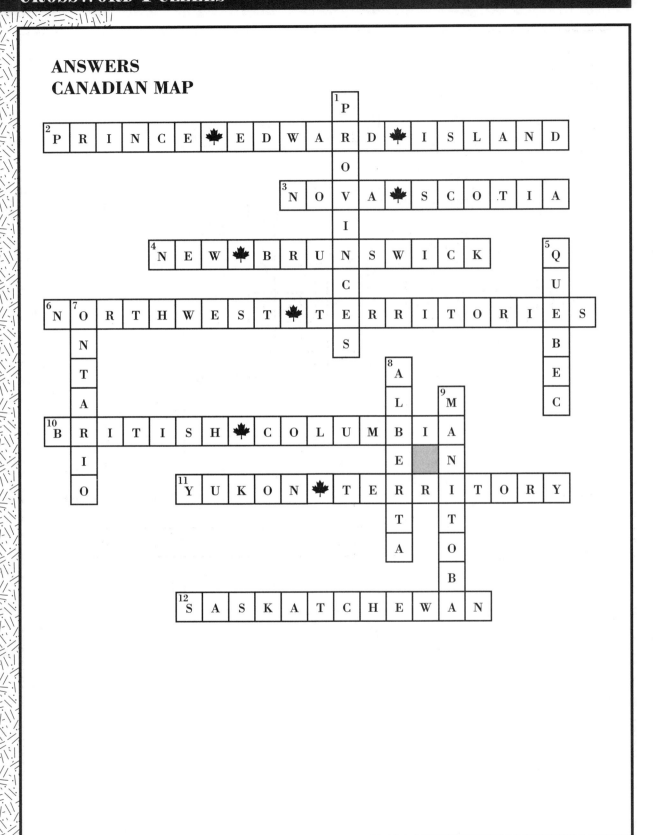

ANSWERS
OPPOSITES ~ NOUNS

ANSWERS
OPPOSITES ~ ADJECTIVES AND ADVERBS

ANSWERS
OPPOSITES ~ VERBS

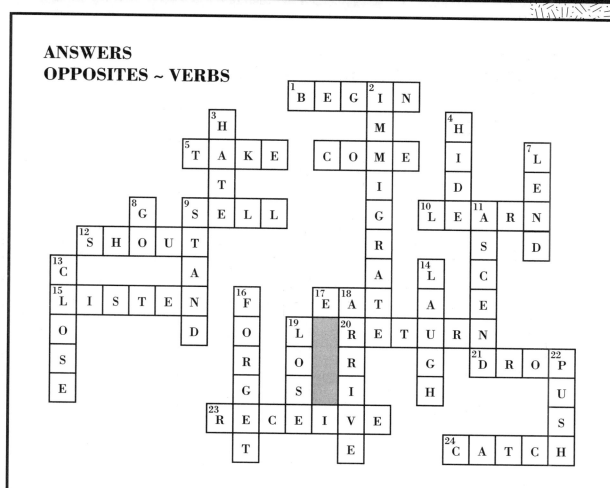

CROSSWORD PUZZLES

ANSWERS
VERBS ~ IRREGULAR PAST

Level ~ Beginner/Intermediate

These games are used as a **grammar review**.

PRE-ACTIVITY

Make sure students are familiar with the basics of how to play a sequential-square board game. The marker starts outside the playing area. Move the marker the number of squares directed. Start each move from the square in which the marker is resting and begin counting with the next square.

Review the following vocabulary with the students:
shuffle the cards
face down
to the right/to the left
disagree

GENERAL DIRECTIONS

1. Students play each game with a partner. If a group of three or four will be playing the game, change your oral directions.

2. Distribute copies of the **Up and Down Game Board** so that there is one for each group. For permanence and more durability, use your photocopier to enlarge the game board onto thin cardboard and laminate it.

3. For each group, copy a set of game pages and cut them along the dotted lines to make playing cards. For permanent sets, copy these pages onto thin cardboard.

4. Provide coloured markers or different Canadian coins for playing pieces. Alternatively, the students can supply their own coins as playing pieces. Dice are not needed.

Give the following directions to the students:

Note: Each game will have its own instructions for step 2.

1. Shuffle the playing cards to mix them well. Turn them face down on the table.

2. Partner A will choose a card. (See each game for further specific directions.)

3. Partner B decides whether or not the answer is correct. You will be the judge only if they disagree.

4. If Partner A is right, he or she moves the marker the number of spaces shown on the right-hand side of the card and stops. If he or she stops on a square that instructs to "Go up," he or she moves up to that square. Partner A's turn is now finished. If he or she stops on a square that instructs to "Go down," he or she moves down to that square. Partner A's turn is now finished. If Partner A is incorrect, he or she does not move.

5. Partner B then chooses a card and gives the answer. Partner A decides if it is correct, and, if it is, Partner B moves.

6. The first person to reach 100 is the winner.

Note: You, the teacher, will only referee if there is a dispute. Students themselves are responsible for judging if a partner's answer is right or wrong.

ADDITIONAL ACTIVITIES (for all games)

For all Additional Activities, use only the clue pages or teacher-made cards from a game.

1. The teacher reads the card and the students take turns orally giving the correct answer.

2. *A listening exercise* ~ The teacher reads out loud what is on the card. Students write down the correct answer.

3. To fill the last ten minutes of a class, divide a small class into two teams. Have a "Bee." The first player chooses a card and gives an answer; if she or he is right, the team gets a point. The next team has a turn. Alternate until the students have answered a reasonable number of questions or until everyone has had a turn.

PLURALS

Specific Instructions for Step 2.

Read the word on the card out loud and then say the plural of the word. Most of the answers will be irregular. Very few are regular.

Variations

1. Spell the answer either orally or by writing it down.
2. Give a sentence using the plural form of the word.
3. Make a question using the plural form of the word.

ABBREVIATIONS

Specific Instructions for Step 2.

Look at the abbreviation, or short form, on the card and give the meaning of the abbreviation.

Variations

1. Write the complete word(s) for which the abbreviation stands.
2. Give the meaning of the abbreviation and then use the abbreviation in a sentence.

CONTRACTIONS

Specific Instructions for Step 2.

Say the words on the card and then give the contraction for the words.

Variations

1. Give the contraction and use it in a sentence.
2. Give the contraction in the interrogative form.
3. Make up a sentence using the contraction as a tag ending.

MAKING QUESTIONS

Note: This is for High Intermediate students. It is a difficult exercise, and students should be familiar with making questions. It is highly recommended that students practise with some answer/question activities before playing this game.

PRE-ACTIVITY

Write the following words on the blackboard:

Who / What / Where / Why / When / How

How many / How long / How often / What kind

Whom / To whom

Explain that the questions must start with one of these words or word phrases. Leave these words on the board for students' reference during the game.

Specific Instructions for Step 2.

Look at the sentence on the card. It is the answer to a question. Read the sentence out loud and then give the question for that answer. The underlined words give a hint about which question word you should use.

Make copies of the *Student Reference Sheet* at the end of this text available if you think it will help your students.

Variations

1. Write the question down.
2. Students make up their own game page. Each student writes five answers and underlines part of the answer. The other students must ask the appropriate question for that answer.

PART B

STUDENT PUZZLES

The answers to all of these clues are **red** or they are connected with the colour **red**. Read the clue. Write the answer in the box beside the clue.

1. You put this on your hot dog or your hamburger to make it taste better.	
2. You see this traffic sign on the corner of a street.	
3. You see this object in the centre of the Canadian flag.	
4. This crisp and sweet fruit with a red skin grows in Canada. You'll find them growing on trees in the west and in the east.	
5. You can drink this liquid with dinner. It's made from grapes.	
6. When you think of blue, you think of cold. When you think of red, you think of this.	
7. Most people think this sweet, juicy fruit is a vegetable. It grows in Canadian gardens in the summer.	
8. Sprinkle this spice in your sauces to make them extra hot!	

Now, match these pictures with some of the clues. Put the number of the clue under the picture.

#_____   #_____   #_____   #_____

The answers to all of these clues are **orange** or they are connected with the colour **orange**. Read the clue. Write the answer in the box beside the clue.

1. This fruit is very juicy. It does not grow in Canada, but we can buy it in stores all year long.	
2. You will see many of these things in the fall in Canada, especially in eastern Canada. They make the trees bright.	
3. This hot object can keep you warm on a cold winter night.	
4. Rabbits love this long, crispy vegetable that grows in Canadian gardens.	
5. At the end of October you can cut a funny face in this object for Hallowe'en.	
6. This good food is made from milk.	
7. This small fruit is very easy to peel and it's good to eat.	
8. You can drink this at breakfast.	

Now, match these pictures with some of the clues. Put the number of the clue under the picture.

#_____   #_____   #_____   #_____

The answers to all of these clues are **yellow** or they are connected with the colour **yellow**. Read the clue. Write the answer in the box beside the clue.

1. This large star gives us our day.	
2. This is part of an egg.	
3. You put this sauce on a hot dog or a hamburger.	
4. Monkeys love this fruit; many people do too.	
5. This citrus fruit is small and sour.	
6. This citrus fruit is a little sweeter and much larger.	
7. If you have lots of this item, maybe you are rich.	
8. This bright flower grows well in the Canadian spring.	

Now, match these pictures with some of the clues. Put the number of the clue under the picture.

#_____   #_____   #_____   #_____

The answers to all of these clues are **green** or they are connected with the colour **green**. Read the clue. Write the answer in the box beside the clue.

1. This very small plant grows all over the world.	
2. This tells you to "go" when you are on a street corner.	
3. You will like eating this fruit. It makes good wine too!	
4. This grows on all trees.	
5. These little round vegetables are sweet.	
6. This is another vegetable that grows well in Canadian gardens. It's long and thin.	
7. Another vegetable! You can use it in salads. Big ones are round and hollow. Very small ones are hot and spicy.	
8. This is a small animal that lives in or near the water. It hops and eats flies.	

Now, match these pictures with some of the clues. Put the number of the clue under the picture.

#_____

#_____

#_____

#_____

The answers to all of these clues are **blue** or they are connected with the colour **blue**. Read the clue. Write the answer in the box beside the clue.

1. Look up! It is everywhere above you on a nice day.	
2. Some people see with them.	
3. This is a large body of water. There are thousands of them in Canada.	
4. These are a kind of pants that many Canadians like to wear.	
5. This bird is seen in many parts of Canada in the fall and winter. It loves to eat sunflower seeds.	
6. You can find this small berry in the late summer. It makes delicious pies and jams.	
7. A pen uses this liquid.	
8. This object is very small. You find it in a nest of a special bird that comes to Canada in the spring and stays all summer.	

Now, match these pictures with some of the clues. Put the number of the clue under the picture.

#_____   #_____   #_____   #_____

The answers to all of these clues are **purple** or they are connected with the colour **purple**. Read the clue. Write the answer in the box beside the clue.

1. This fruit grows in bunches. It makes good juice and wine.	
2. Sometimes we call this vegetable by its French name, aubergine.	
3. In Canada, this sweet smelling flower blooms early in the spring. It grows on a bush.	
4. The leaves of this vegetable make a large, round ball. You cook and eat these leaves.	
5. What a pretty little flower! It grows early in the spring, close to the ground.	
6. This fruit grows on a tree. It is ready to pick in the late summer.	

Now, match these pictures with some of the clues. Put the number of the clue under the picture.

#_____   #_____   #_____   #_____

The answers to all of these clues are **black** or they are connected with the colour **black**. Read the clue. Write the answer in the box beside the clue.

1. Cars, buses, and trucks drive on this.	
2. This large bird doesn't sing very well. Canada has a lot of this kind of bird in the spring, summer, and fall.	
3. You use this to make foods spicy. It is salt's partner.	
4. Think of four round objects on a car.	
5. This is the time when the stars shine, if the sky is clear.	
6. Some people drink this in the morning with their breakfast.	
7. This part of your body can also be brown, red, blonde, or white.	
8. You use this liquid in machines. In Canada, it is found in Alberta and Newfoundland.	

Now, match these pictures with some of the clues. Put the number of the clue under the picture.

#_____   #_____   #_____   #_____

> The answers to all of these clues are **brown** or they are connected with the colour **brown**. Read the clue. Write the answer in the box beside the clue.

1. Some people love to eat this candy. It is sometimes sweet and sometimes bitter.	
2. You put flowers and other plants in this.	
3. For some people, these let them see.	
4. This large farm animal can give you milk. It can also be brown and white or black and white.	
5. This food is good for you! You can buy it in the bakery section of a supermarket.	
6. This part of your body is long, short, straight, or curly.	
7. A lot of furniture is made from this.	
8. Children in Canada love to eat this kind of sandwich with jam or jelly.	

> Now, match these pictures with some of the clues. Put the number of the clue under the picture.

#_____   #_____   #_____   #_____

The answers to all of these clues are **white** or they are connected with the colour **white**. Read the clue. Write the answer in the box beside the clue.

1. Look up in the sky for these objects.	
2. In winter, a lot of Canada is covered with this cold stuff.	
3. Use a lot of this material in school.	
4. Put these on your feet before you put on your shoes.	
5. Prince Edward Island is famous for this vegetable. It has a brown skin and is white inside.	
6. Many people use this spice when they are cooking meat and vegetables. It is pepper's partner.	
7. What a good and healthy drink!	
8. Make things taste sweet with this.	
9. A large animal living in Canada's north.	
10. This basic food is served instead of potatoes or noodles.	

Now, match these pictures with some of the clues. Put the number of the clue under the picture.

#_____   #_____   #_____   #_____

Look at each group of words. One word in each group does not belong. Find the word and circle it. Be ready to explain why it does not belong.

1. ears   nose   eyes   feet   mouth

2. skirt   dress   shirt   blouse   nightgown

3. glass   cup   meat   bowl   plate

4. milk   cheese   yogurt   cream   fish

5. pencil   paper   chalk   pen   crayon

6. book   letter   paper   pen   newspaper

7. tea   coffee   milk   juice   sandwich

8. crow   cat   dog   cow   horse

9. shoe   boot   coat   slipper   runner

10. lunch   supper   egg   dinner   breakfast

Look at each line of words. One word in each line does not belong to the group. Find the word and circle it. Be ready to explain why it does not belong.

1. box   bag   pot   glove   purse

2. wind   cloud   rain   tree   snow

3. apple   orange   potato   cherry   pear

4. car   truck   bus   taxi   airplane

5. house   tent   apartment school   townhouse

6. sky   grass   leaves   peas   beans

7. uncle   father   aunt   brother   grandfather

8. meat   pie   pudding   cake   ice cream

9. Ottawa   Paris   London   Canada   Washington

10. table   chair   books   pencil   students

Look at each line of words. One word in each line does not belong to the group. Find the word and circle it. Be ready to explain why it does not belong.

1.	pot	pan	skillet	spoon	frying pan
2.	potato	carrot	bean	pea	pear
3.	coat	dress	hat	mitts	boots
4.	bed	stove	sink	cupboard	refrigerator
5.	floor	ceiling	door	wall	roof
6.	pen	paper	computer	pencil	typewriter
7.	mother	father	brother	friend	sister
8.	cold	warm	hot	cool	rain
9.	body	cold	flu	mumps	chicken pox
10.	Spain	England	U.S.A.	Canada	Australia

> Look at each line of words. One word in each line does not belong to the group. Find the word and circle it. Be ready to explain why it does not belong.

1. Bolivia   Mexico   Brazil   Colombia   Peru
2. guitar   violin   trumpet   harp   piano
3. rose   daffodil   tulip   violet   cauliflower
4. shampoo   dishtowel   soap   bath towel   facecloth
5. cup   plate   mug   jug   wineglass
6. coat   jacket   sweater   shirt   sock
7. cake   peas   pie   pudding   fruit
8. elephant   giraffe   whale   mouse   hippopotamus
9. poppy   tomato   blood   carrot   stop sign
10. country   lake   ocean   river   sea

Look at each line of words. One word in each line does not belong to the group. Find the word and circle it. Be ready to explain why it does not belong.

Think hard ~ These choices are difficult!

1. flour   sugar   pepper   salt   cinnamon

2. orange   grape   lemon   lime   grapefruit

3. dog   ape   deer   bear   cat

4. tomato   potato   peanut   turnip   carrot

5. chicken   cow   goat   pig   squirrel

6. house   school   office   park   playground

7. clouds   grass   airplane   tower   skyscraper

8. leaf   flower   grass   zucchini   peas

9. ear   nose   arm   leg   eye

10. chalk   milk   salt   sugar   chocolate

Look at each line of words. One word in each line does not belong to the group. Find the word and circle it. Be ready to explain why it does not belong.

Careful ~ these are tricky grammar puzzles!
Think about singular and plural.
Think about nouns and verbs.
Think about adjectives and adverbs.
Think about positive and negative.

1.	go	come	eat	to	drink
2.	I	in	on	at	for
3.	quickly	quietly	slowly	fast	suddenly
4.	we	you	I	they	us
5.	house	horses	cars	schools	buses
6.	sing	song	sings	singing	sang
7.	jumped	danced	walked	ran	moved
8.	school	teach	student	teacher	room
9.	province	capital	country	city	free
10.	stopped	liked	fitted	robbed	planned

Look at each line of words. One word in each line does not belong to the group. Find the word and circle it. Be ready to explain why it does not belong.

Careful ~ these are tricky grammar puzzles!
Think about singular and plural.
Think about nouns and verbs.
Think about adjectives and adverbs.
Think about positive and negative.

1. girls
   boys
   men
   ladies
   woman

2. house
   car
   buses
   train
   road

3. isn't
   can't
   won't
   aren't
   can

4. will
   was
   found
   were
   played

5. sang
   came
   drove
   play
   wrote

6. big
   small
   little
   huge
   elephant

7. bus driver
   firefighter
   homemaker
   doctor
   police officer

8. teeth
   leg
   feet
   knees
   heels

9. went
   saw
   wrote
   found
   stopped

10. brown
    table
    chair
    floor
    tree

First look at the words in each line. Then look at the words in the box at the bottom of the page. Choose a word from the box that has something in common with the other words on the line. Write the word on the blank at the end of each line.

1. cat   dog   bird   hamster   _____

2. legs   arms   hands   feet   _____

3. eyes   ears   nose   mouth   _____

4. mother   father   son   daughter   _____

5. yellow   green   blue   purple   _____

6. stove   sink   oven   refrigerator _____

7. noun   adverb   adjective preposition   _____

8. breakfast   lunch   dinner   supper   _____

9. penny   dime   quarter   nickel   _____

10. sweater   blouse   skirt   jeans   _____

cheeks	**counter**	**dress**	**fish**
grandmother	**knees**	**loony**	**red**
	snack	**verb**	

First look at the words in each line. Then look at the words in the box at the bottom of the page. Choose a word from the box that has something in common with the other words on the line. Write the word on the blank at the end of each line.

1. red   yellow   blue   green   _____

2. tea   water   coffee   juice   _____

3. car   bus   taxi   truck   _____

4. desk   chair   book   pencil   _____

5. shoe   boot   skate   sneaker   _____

6. arm   leg   foot   shoulder   _____

7. Winni-   White-   Frederic-   Charlotte-   _____
    peg   horse   ton   town

8. I   you   we   they   _____

9. rain   snow   cloud   sunshine   _____

10. chicken   cow   horse   goat   _____

bicycle	eraser	fog	hand
milk	pig	purple	she
	sock	Yellowknife	

First look at the words in each line. Then look at the words in the box at the bottom of the page. Choose a word from the box that has something in common with the other words on the line. Write the word on the blank at the end of each line.

1. man   woman   boy   girl   _____

2. house   tent   cave   townhouse   _____

3. apple   plum   peach   cherry   _____

4. car   bus   train   truck   _____

5. robin   bluejay   sparrow   crow   _____

6. cold   warm   hot   cool   _____

7. Canada   U.S.A.   England   Australia   _____

8. kitchen   bathroom   bedroom   living room _____

9. rose   daffodil   crocus   tulip   _____

10. mouth   nose   ear   hair   _____

apartment	baby	forehead	chickadee
daisy	dining room	freezing	Ireland
	pear	taxi	

First look at the words in each line. Then look at the words in the box at the bottom of the page. Choose a word from the box that has something in common with the other words on the line. Write the word on the blank at the end of each line.

1. niece   nephew   aunt   uncle   _____

2. book   letter   magazine   newspaper   _____

3. cup   glass   mug   bottle   _____

4. pencil   crayon   pen   marker   _____

5. clerk   grocer   firefighter police officer _____

6. books   pens   lessons   students   _____

7. butter   yogurt   cream   milk   _____

8. eggs   cereal   toast   bacon   _____

9. dollar   lira   pound   franc   _____

10. Toronto   Victoria   Edmonton   Halifax   _____

can	chalk	electrician	grandmother
ice cream	note	pancakes	teachers
Quebec City	yen		

First look at the words in each line. Then look at the words in the box at the bottom of the page. Choose a word from the box that has something in common with the other words on the line. Write the word on the blank at the end of each line.

1. father   nephew   son   brother   _____

2. violin   flute   drum   harp   _____

3. mother   sister   aunt   daughter   _____

4. bird   airplane   butterfly   jet   _____

5. fish   whale   turtle   penguin   _____

6. armchair   sofa   stool   deck chair _____

7. canoe   ship   raft   submarine   _____

8. shower   bath   pool   rain   _____

9. France   Germany   Austria   Italy   _____

10. letter   telephone   fax   telegram   _____

bat   bench   clarinet   conversation

niece   river   seal   sailboat

Spain   uncle

First look at the words in each line. Then look at the words in the box at the bottom of the page. Choose a word from the box that has something in common with the other words on the line. Write the word on the blank at the end of each line.

1. carrot   beet   turnip   potato   _____

2. orange   ball   marble   moon   _____

3. mango   grapefruit banana   orange   _____

4. oregano   thyme   parsley   sage   _____

5. rice   bulgur   oats   couscous   _____

6. lettuce   spinach   beans   peas   _____

7. plum   apple   peach   pear   _____

8. beef   pork   lamb   goat   _____

9. cookie   clock   plate   quarter   _____

10. cake   pie   pudding   cheese   _____

apricot	basil	basketball	cabbage
camel	cookies	lid	onion
	pineapple	wheat	

FEELINGS

happy	hungry	cold	embarrassed
sad	sick	scared	brave
angry	healthy	lonely	surprised
tired	nervous	proud	relaxed

The words in the box are feelings that we all have. Some feelings are pleasant; others are not so nice to have.

Put the words from the box in the right category. Some words may belong on more than one list. Be ready to explain why you put the words where you did.

Good Feelings

_____

_____

_____

_____

_____

_____

_____

_____

Bad Feelings

_____

_____

_____

_____

_____

_____

_____

_____

FOOD

roast beef	popcorn	soda pop	milk
potatoes	chips	cake	carrots
coffee	rice	beans	fried egg
chicken	juice	peanuts	hamburger
apple	wine	candy	water
grapes	noodles	fish	ice cream

All the words in the box are different kinds of food or drink. Some are foods you eat for a meal, while others you eat only for a snack. A third category is not food to eat but something to drink.

Put the words from the box in the right category. Some words may belong on more than one list. Be ready to explain why you put the words where you did.

Meals	Drinks	Snacks
_____	_____	_____
_____	_____	_____
_____	_____	_____
_____	_____	_____
_____	_____	_____
_____	_____	_____
_____	_____	_____
_____	_____	_____
_____	_____	_____
_____	_____	_____

ROOMS OF THE HOUSE

bed	chair	table	lamp
rug	stove	blanket	dresser
sofa	dishes	drapes	refrigerator
cupboard	pillow	sheet	pots
mattress	sink	shelf	mirror

You can find the objects in the above box in different rooms of the house.

Put the words from the box in the right category. Some words may belong on more than one list. Be ready to explain why you put the words where you did.

Living Room	Kitchen	Bedroom
_____	_____	_____
_____	_____	_____
_____	_____	_____
_____	_____	_____
_____	_____	_____
_____	_____	_____
_____	_____	_____
_____	_____	_____
_____	_____	_____

CANADIAN ANIMALS

beaver	fish	cat	butterfly
horse	cow	goat	dog
frog	whale	skunk	grasshopper
chicken	snake	squirrel	robin
bluejay	sheep	moose	polar bear
turtle	duck	deer	cougar
ant	crow	raccoon	crab

All the animals in the above box live in Canada. Some of these animals only move on the ground. Some fly in the air. Others spend their time in the water. Do you know these Canadian animals?

Put the words from the box in the right category. How does each move? Some animals may belong on more than one list. Be ready to tell why you put the words where you did.

On The Ground   **In The Air**   **In The Water**

CITIES AND COUNTRIES

Brazil	Canada	India	Moscow
Canton	England	Japan	Nigeria
China	Fredericton	Lebanon	Ottawa
Calgary	Guatemala	Mexico	Paris
	Victoria	Quebec	

▶ The words in the box are either cities or countries.

Put the words from the box in the right category. Some words may belong on more than one list. Be ready to explain why you put the words where you did.

Cities   **Countries**

_____   _____

_____   _____

_____   _____

_____   _____

_____   _____

_____   _____

_____   _____

_____   _____

MALE AND FEMALE

aunt	father	Mr.	secretary
baby	grandma	Mrs.	sister
brother	grandpa	Ms.	son
cousin	husband	nephew	teacher
daughter	mother	niece	uncle
doctor	Miss	nurse	wife

The words in the box are male or female.

Put the words from the box in the right category. Some words may belong on more than one list. Be ready to explain why you put the words where you did.

Male   **Female**

_____   _____
_____   _____
_____   _____
_____   _____
_____   _____
_____   _____
_____   _____
_____   _____
_____   _____
_____   _____
_____   _____
_____   _____
_____   _____

THE SENSES

rose	music	fire	radio
orange	candy	sea water	soft
kitten	smooth	chocolate	cheese
itch	good news	garlic	wet dog
blue sky	good wine	books	birds
rough	cold	dead fish	hard

You need your senses for these words. Some things you can only see with your eyes; some you can only hear with your ears. You can smell or taste others, and some you can feel. For some of them, you can use more than one of your senses.

Put the words from the box in the right category. Some words may belong on more than one list. Be ready to explain why you put the words where you did.

See	Hear	Smell	Taste	Feel
_____	_____	_____	_____	_____
_____	_____	_____	_____	_____
_____	_____	_____	_____	_____
_____	_____	_____	_____	_____
_____	_____	_____	_____	_____
_____	_____	_____	_____	_____
_____	_____	_____	_____	_____
_____	_____	_____	_____	_____
_____	_____	_____	_____	_____

NOUNS AND VERBS

sing	song	teach	letter
walk	cat	learn	watch
learner	reader	teacher	come
read	work	lake	like
worker	see	write	cut

The words in the box are nouns (name words) or verbs (action words). Be careful! Some of these words are tricky.

Put the words from the box in the right category. Some words may belong on more than one list. Be ready to explain why you put the words where you did.

Nouns   **Verbs**

_____   _____

_____   _____

_____   _____

_____   _____

_____   _____

_____   _____

_____   _____

_____   _____

_____   _____

_____   _____

_____   _____

SINGULAR AND PLURAL

children	foot	moose	mouse
pen	lesson	men	teeth
man	mice	women	woman
child	glasses	tooth	feet
people	geese	bus	fish

The words in the box are one thing (singular) or more than one (plural).

Put the words from the box in the right category. Some words may belong on more than one list. Be ready to explain why you put the words where you did.

Singular   **Plural**

_____   _____

_____   _____

_____   _____

_____   _____

_____   _____

_____   _____

_____   _____

_____   _____

_____   _____

_____   _____

_____   _____

_____   _____

SINCE... FOR...

two weeks	three hours
last week	Tuesday night
nine days	2:30
a long time	I came home
now	I left my country
Wednesday	the rest of my life
9 o'clock	the rest of the year
the night	the beginning of May

▶ The words in the above box follow **since...** or **for...** . Put the words from the box in the right category. Some words may belong on more than one list. Be ready to explain why you put the words where you did.

Since. . .

_____

_____

_____

_____

_____

_____

_____

_____

_____

For. . .

_____

_____

_____

_____

_____

_____

_____

_____

_____

A category is a group of things that are alike. After each category name, write five words that belong in the category. You can use words you know or you can use a dictionary or other books to help you.

1. Colours

   blue _____   red _____   green _____   yellow _____   purple _____

2. Cities

   _____   _____   _____   _____   _____

3. Countries

   _____   _____   _____   _____   _____

4. Family members

   _____   _____   _____   _____   _____

5. Teachers

   _____   _____   _____   _____   _____

6. Street names

   _____   _____   _____   _____   _____

7. Provinces

   _____   _____   _____   _____   _____

8. Animals

   _____   _____   _____   _____   _____

9. Fruit

   _____   _____   _____   _____   _____

10. Vegetables

   _____   _____   _____   _____   _____

A category is a group of things that are alike. After each category name, write five words that belong in the category. You can use words you know or you can use a dictionary or other books to help you.

1. Numbers under 20

   _____   _____   _____   _____   _____

2. Days of the week

   _____   _____   _____   _____   _____

3. Cars

   _____   _____   _____   _____   _____

4. Subjects in school

   _____   _____   _____   _____   _____

5. Cities in Canada

   _____   _____   _____   _____   _____

6. Rooms in a house

   _____   _____   _____   _____   _____

7. Weather words

   _____   _____   _____   _____   _____

8. Farm animals

   _____   _____   _____   _____   _____

9. Birds

   _____   _____   _____   _____   _____

10. Months

   _____   _____   _____   _____   _____

A category is a group of things that are alike. After each category name, write five words that belong in the category. You can use words you know or you can use a dictionary or other books to help you.

1. Occupations

   _____ _____ _____ _____ _____

2. Small mammals

   _____ _____ _____ _____ _____

3. Large mammals

   _____ _____ _____ _____ _____

4. Fish

   _____ _____ _____ _____ _____

5. Illnesses

   _____ _____ _____ _____ _____

6. Sweet things to eat

   _____ _____ _____ _____ _____

7. Buildings or other places to live in

   _____ _____ _____ _____ _____

8. Sports

   _____ _____ _____ _____ _____

9. Capital cities

   _____ _____ _____ _____ _____

10. Drinks

   _____ _____ _____ _____ _____

A category is a group of things that are alike. After each category name, write five words that belong in the category. You can use words you know or you can use a dictionary or other books to help you.

1. Old things

   _____ _____ _____ _____ _____

2. Modern things

   _____ _____ _____ _____ _____

3. Musical instruments

   _____ _____ _____ _____ _____

4. Countries in South America

   _____ _____ _____ _____ _____

5. Holidays

   _____ _____ _____ _____ _____

6. Kinds of buildings

   _____ _____ _____ _____ _____

7. Canadian coins

   _____ _____ _____ _____ _____

8. Oceans

   _____ _____ _____ _____ _____

9. Rivers in Canada

   _____ _____ _____ _____ _____

10. Countries in Africa

   _____ _____ _____ _____ _____

A category is a group of things that are alike. After each category name, write five words that belong in the category. You can use words you know or you can use a dictionary or other books to help you.

1. Vowels

   _____   _____   _____   _____   _____

2. Verbs

   _____   _____   _____   _____   _____

3. Nouns

   _____   _____   _____   _____   _____

4. Adjectives

   _____   _____   _____   _____   _____

5. Pronouns

   _____   _____   _____   _____   _____

6. Prepositions

   _____   _____   _____   _____   _____

7. Words with double vowels

   _____   _____   _____   _____   _____

8. Adverbs

   _____   _____   _____   _____   _____

9. Big words

   _____   _____   _____   _____   _____

10. Words with double consonants

    _____   _____   _____   _____   _____

A C E H M N
O Q S T V Y

> Use the letters above to make words. Put one letter in each space.
> You may only use each letter once!

	ewfoundland
	anada
	ntario
	uebec
	alifax
	ukon

	askatchewan
	lberta
	oronto
	ancouver
	anitoba
	dmonton

What is a good name for this puzzle?

_____

b c d e f g
h l m p r s

▶ Use the letters above to make words. Put one letter in each space.
You may only use each letter once!

	orse
	oat
	ow
	accoon
	og
	eaver

	orcupine
	ion
	oose
	quirrel
	lephant
	ox

What is a good name for this puzzle?

_____

b   c   d   e   g   h
j   o   p   r   s   w

▶ Use the letters above to make words. Put one letter in each space.
You may only use each letter once!

	obin			parrow
	igeon			oodpecker
	ay			wl
	row			uck
	awk			ull
	agle			lackbird

What is a good name for this puzzle?

_____

b   c   d   e   f   l
m   p   r   s   t   w

▶ Use the letters above to make words. Put one letter in each space.
You may only use each letter once!

	eacher		raser
	uler		alls
	essons		ap
	riends		en
	ooks		hair
	esk		tudent

What is a good name for this puzzle?

_____

a   b   c   d   f   g
h   k   l   r   s   w

▶ Use the letters above to make words. Put one letter in each space.
You may only use each letter once!

	oom
	edroom
	loset
	loor
	ttic
	ights

	itchen
	all
	oor
	alls
	tairs
	as

What is a good name for this puzzle?

_____

b   c   d   f   g   l
p   r   s   t   w   y

▶ Use the letters above to make words. Put one letter in each space.
You may only use each letter once!

	oof
	indow
	ard
	ree
	irds
	teps

	oor
	rass
	ence
	lants
	awn
	hildren

What is a good name for this puzzle?

_____

b   c   d   f   k   l
m   o   p   s   t   w

> Use the letters above to make words. Put one letter in each space.
> You may only use each letter once!

	ishes			ink
	ven			upboard
	ot			icrowave
	indow			able
	nife			ork
	owl			ight

What is a good name for this puzzle?

_____

b c d f h l
m n p s t w

▶ Use the letters above to make words. Put one letter in each space.
You may only use each letter once!

	armer
	urse
	echanic
	ook
	octor
	eacher

	omemaker
	ecretary
	awyer
	riter
	us driver
	harmacist

What is a good name for this puzzle?

_____

▶ **All your answers will begin with the letter "A."**

1. It is a fruit you can find in Canada in the late summer and early fall.	
2. This western province's capital is Edmonton.	
3. It's a large continent across the Atlantic Ocean from South America.	
4. He works in the movies and on television.	
5. This is the number of the place where you live.	
6. It is between your foot and your leg.	
7. Maybe you wear this item when you work in the kitchen.	
8. The time between noon and 6 p.m.	
9. Airplanes come to and go from this place.	
10. Perhaps you use this book of maps.	
11. A small, black insect.	
12. It is between your shoulder and your hand.	

▶ All your answers will begin with the letter "B."

1. It's bigger than a car. Maybe you came to school on this.	
2. You use this item to cover a cut when you hurt yourself.	
3. This Canadian animal is on the back of a nickel.	
4. This western province touches the Pacific Ocean.	
5. A pretty shirt for a woman.	
6. You wear them on your feet in the rain or snow.	
7. It's the colour of the sky on a nice day.	
8. A child's toy. It's round and it bounces.	
9. This animal is covered with feathers.	
10. This person makes bread, cakes, and pies.	
11. A long, yellow fruit. Monkeys love it.	
12. A pretty insect that flies in your garden.	

▶ All your answers will begin with the letter "C."

1. A person who is a citizen of Canada.	
2. The opposite of "hot."	
3. This object tells you the time.	
4. On a cool day, you put this item on before you go out to school or work.	
5. This animal gives milk.	
6. A pretty, yellow bird that sings. In Canada, you can keep it as a pet.	
7. A long, narrow boat that you move by using paddles.	
8. You see these white things in the sky. They are grey when it rains.	
9. It's in the middle of an apple or a pear.	
10. A large country north of the United States.	
11. You put your tea or coffee in this object.	
12. The opposite of "open."	

DdDdD

▶ All your answers will begin with the letter "D."

1. This person works in a hospital and helps you when you are sick.	
2. The last month of the year.	
3. You can have this animal as a pet.	
4. This person cleans and fixes your teeth.	
5. This red apple grows in the Okanagan Valley in British Columbia.	
6. The opposite of "night."	
7. A large, hot, sandy place.	
8. The paper money you spend in Canada.	
9. The way into a house or school.	
10. The way you move to music.	
11. This is the food that you sometimes eat at the end of a meal.	
12. The opposite of "up."	

▶ All your answers will begin with the letter "E."

1. You have two of these things and you use them to listen.	
2. The opposite of "late."	
3. This sign shows you the way out.	
4. The opposite of "west."	
5. It has a hard shell. You use it in cooking.	
6. One more than seventy-nine.	
7. You use these parts of your face to see.	
8. The opposite of "beginning."	
9. The planet where we live.	
10. This is the capital city of Alberta, Canada.	
11. It lets you bend your arm.	
12. You use this object to fix your mistakes when you write your English exercises.	

▶ **All your answers will begin with the letter "F."**

1. It comes after four.	
2. It's another name for autumn and leaves do this in Canada in the autumn too.	
3. You have five on each hand.	
4. This animal swims in the water.	
5. Your eyes, nose, and mouth are here.	
6. You walk on this in a room.	
7. The opposite of "back."	
8. Your mother, father, sisters, brothers, and you make this.	
9. These pretty plants grow in your garden.	
10. Everything you eat!	
11. The opposite of "mother."	
12. You know and like this person but he or she is not in your family.	

All your answers will begin with the letter "G."

1. This is a large, round, yellow citrus fruit.	
2. This is the colour of grass.	
3. A mechanic works in this building.	
4. This small insect jumps through the grass.	
5. The oldest people in your family.	
6. This liquid makes cars, buses, and trucks go.	
7. Pour your milk, water, or juice in this container so you can drink it.	
8. A large, black-haired mammal that walks on two legs. It lives in Africa.	
9. This yellow metal is used to make coins and jewellery.	
10. The opposite of "boy."	
11. You wear these to help you see.	
12. Horses, cows, and sheep like to eat this small plant.	

▶ All your answers will begin with the letter "H."

1. A part of the body just below the waist.	
2. This is found at the top of your body.	
3. Everyone enjoys this time off from work or school.	
4. The opposite of "cold."	
5. A high piece of land that rhymes with "will."	
6. The capital city of Nova Scotia, Canada.	
7. A covering for the head.	
8. The opposite of "wife."	
9. This dried grass is fed to farm animals.	
10. This part of the arm is below the wrist.	
11. Bees make this sweet, sticky, yellowish liquid.	
12. In Canadian education, grades nine to twelve.	

▶ All your answers will begin with the letter "I."

1. Frozen water.	
2. A preposition with many uses.	
3. Negative form of the verb "to be," third person, singular.	
4. Canada's first northern people.	
5. This feeling on your skin makes you want to scratch.	
6. These very small animals live everywhere in the world.	
7. This is what Canada's smallest province is.	
8. You use this object to press your clothes.	
9. The contraction of "it is."	
10. The liquid in a pen.	
11. Something serious is also this.	
12. This word means "sick."	

▶ All your answers will begin with the letter "J."

1. This is something you have so you can earn money.	
2. Rings, bracelets, and necklaces.	
3. A very common man's name in Canada.	
4. Some immigrants come from this far eastern country.	
5. This is a short coat with sleeves.	
6. This airplane is very fast.	
7. The first month of the year.	
8. You get this liquid when you squeeze fruit.	
9. The month before July.	
10. This person looks after and cleans a building.	
11. Many Canadians like to wear these pants, especially teenagers.	
12. A glass container with a screw-on lid.	

All your answers will begin with the letter "K."

1. A tomato sauce you can put on hamburgers or hot dogs.	
2. The opposite of "queen."	
3. This is how you hit a ball with your foot.	
4. You use this to lock and unlock your door.	
5. A school for young children, before they start grade one.	
6. This lets your leg bend. (Be careful with the spelling of this one!)	
7. Where you cook your meals.	
8. This is a young goat or a young child (slang).	
9. The past tense of "keep."	
10. The sacred book of the Muslim faith.	
11. This is a baby cat.	
12. This is a child's toy that flies in the wind.	

▶ All your answers will begin with the letter "L."

1. You walk using this part of your body.	
2. The opposite of "first."	
3. This is a baby sheep.	
4. This citrus fruit is sour and yellow.	
5. You can find many books in this place.	
6. People climb this object to reach high places.	
7. There are many of these bodies of water in Canada.	
8. The opposite of "right."	
9. This is something you send to your family and friends to tell them all your news.	
10. This part inside your body lets you breathe.	
11. This is the warm feeling that parents feel for their children.	
12. In Canada, we eat this meal at noon.	

▶ All your answers will begin with the letter "M."

1. This province is in the middle of Canada.	
2. Coins and pieces of paper used to buy things.	
3. Many children love to drink this white liquid.	
4. This hair grows under a man's nose.	
5. The opposite of "father."	
6. This is a small, furry animal with a long tail.	
7. The day before Tuesday.	
8. It shines in the sky at night.	
9. This leaf is in the middle of the Canadian flag.	
10. You use this to eat and talk.	
11. These are very high, rocky hills you can see in Alberta and British Columbia.	
12. In the summer, this little insect will bite you.	

▶ **All your answers will begin with the letter "N."**

1. The part of the face above the mouth used for breathing and smelling.	
2. The number before one hundred.	
3. This is Canada's newest province.	
4. Birds make this their home.	
5. This person works in a hospital alongside doctors.	
6. Twelve o'clock in the middle of the day.	
7. This Canadian coin is worth five cents.	
8. This is your brother's daughter.	
9. Opposite of "south."	
10. This is the part of your body between your head and your shoulders.	
11. Opposite of "old."	
12. The time between sunset and sunrise.	

▶ All your answers will begin with the letter "O."

1. A sweet citrus fruit.	
2. The capital city of Canada.	
3. The opposite of "on."	
4. This large bird has its eyes on the front of its face. It hunts at night.	
5. The opposite of "young."	
6. The month before November.	
7. The opposite of "under."	
8. Secretaries work here.	
9. You bake bread or roast meat in this part of your stove.	
10. Another word for "job."	
11. A province in Canada with two capital cities.	
12. The opposite of "in."	

▶ All your answers will begin with the letter "P."

1. A partner for salt.	
2. This black and white bear lives in China.	
3. In Canada, you carve a face in this orange vegetable on Hallowe'en.	
4. This bird from South America can talk!	
5. This is something soft to put under your head when you go to sleep.	
6. The large body of water to the west of British Columbia.	
7. A pie covered with slices of tomato, pepperoni, and cheese.	
8. This person can fix a leak in your sink or toilet.	
9. Your mother and father.	
10. Canada has ten of these.	
11. You write with this object.	
12. This is an animal's hand.	

All your answers will begin with the letter "Q."

1. Canada's French-speaking province.	
2. The opposite of "answer."	
3. A female ruler of a nation or country.	
4. This is another word for "stop."	
5. A warm covering for a bed is called by this name.	
6. An adjective that means "fast."	
7. A duck makes this sound.	
8. This Canadian coin, worth twenty-five cents, has a picture of a caribou on its back.	
9. The opposite of "noisy."	
10. The mark you put at the end of a question.	
11. This is the player who throws the ball in Canadian football.	
12. The capital of the province of Quebec.	

All your answers will begin with the letter "R."

1. This bird with a red breast comes to Canada early in the spring.	
2. This city is the capital of Saskatchewan.	
3. This helps you draw a straight line.	
4. This is a baby's toy.	
5. This is a small carpet.	
6. You don't have to cook if you eat at this place!	
7. These are the mountains in British Columbia and Alberta.	
8. You wear this to keep you dry in the rain.	
9. Small, round pieces of jewellery.	
10. These are dried grapes.	
11. This is a beautiful flower.	
12. A small, hot, red-skinned vegetable used in salads.	

▶ All your answers will begin with the letter "S."

1. This is how you move in water.	
2. These keep your feet warm.	
3. This big star keeps the world warm.	
4. The opposite of "north."	
5. A black and white animal that stinks.	
6. This is another word for a large grocery store.	
7. Canada's warmest season.	
8. The past tense of "to see."	
9. Wheat grows in this Canadian province.	
10. This is your boy child.	
11. This is pepper's partner.	
12. A Canadian winter sport.	

TtTtT

▶ All your answers will begin with the letter "T."

1. You chew your food with these.	
2. He or she helps you learn English!	
3. One of the first flowers that grows in Canada in the spring.	
4. Dry yourself with this after your bath.	
5. The number of months in a year.	
6. This carries many people right across Canada.	
7. The capital of Ontario.	
8. It's hot in the summer and cold in the winter.	
9. You can talk to your family and friends using this object.	
10. The opposite of "give."	
11. A drink made with leaves and hot water.	
12. This is the day before Wednesday.	

▶ All your answers will begin with the letter "U."

1. The opposite of "over."	
2. He's your mother's or father's brother.	
3. You and me.	
4. These are the clothes that you wear right next to your skin.	
5. Opposite of "down."	
6. To take off your clothes.	
7. When something is not at all pretty to look at, it is this.	
8. Old and worn, or second-hand.	
9. If your room is not neat, it is this.	
10. This large country is south of Canada.	
11. When something is not true.	
12. It's another word for "sad."	

V v V v V

▶ **All your answers will begin with the letter "V."**

1. The name given to the letters "a," "e," "i," "o," and "u."	
2. This piece of clothing is a jacket without sleeves.	
3. February 14 is this day of love.	
4. It is a large city on Canada's west coast.	
5. Peas, carrots, and corn are examples of this food.	
6. This pretty, purple wildflower grows early in the spring.	
7. You use this machine to clean your carpet or floor.	
8. Words in English such as "to go," "to come," "to work," and "to learn."	
9. It's the capital of British Columbia.	
10. It's a small town.	
11. You put flowers into this pretty container.	
12. You attach this machine to your television to watch movies.	

▶ All your answers will begin with the letter "W."

1. The hair on a sheep has this name.	
2. A person who serves you in a restaurant has this job.	
3. It is the capital city of Canada's Yukon Territory.	
4. This part of a house is found between two rooms.	
5. The opposite of "dry."	
6. It's a small object that tells you the time.	
7. It is the capital of Manitoba.	
8. The opposite of "man."	
9. This part of the body is below the chest and above the hips.	
10. The opposite of "east."	
11. This food is one of Canada's biggest exports.	
12. A bird's arm and hand.	

▶ All your answers will begin with "X," "Y," or "Z."

1. This long, green vegetable grows in Canada in the summer.	
2. It's Canada's smaller territory.	
3. A very bright colour.	
4. This is a special "picture" of your bones.	
5. This is an animal from Africa. It looks like a horse and is covered in black and white stripes.	
6. Contraction of "you are."	
7. The capital of the Northwest Territories.	
8. The unit of money in Japan has this name.	
9. One less than one is called this.	
10. The opposite of "me."	
11. You use this word to give a positive answer to a question.	
12. The day before today has this name.	

1. A _____ on a _____.

2. _____ went up the _____.

3. _____ for _____.

4. A _____ on a _____.

5. The _____ _____.

6. He_____ on his _____.

7. Throw the _____ at the _____.

8. _____ is _____.

ball	bell	car	cat
fell	hands	hat	hill
Jill	nine	Paul	stands
star	tall	wall	Wine

1. Please _____ the _____.

2. She _____ up the _____.

3. The _____ _____ to the

   _____.

4. _____ for _____.

5. _____ is in _____.

6. Here are _____ _____.

7. _____ has a _____.

8. The _____ is on the _____.

bed	Bob	clock	frog
job	lock	log	man
me	men	picks	ran
sticks	tea	Ted	ten
van			

1. There's the _____ to the _____.

2. _____ is _____.

3. That _____ is _____.

4. _____ has my _____?

5. _____ _____ milk please.

6. Have _____ in the _____.

7. A _____ and a _____ by the _____.

8. A _____ for a _____.

ball	Dick	doll	door
fun	house	mine	more
mouse	Pour	shoe	sick
store	sun	wall	Who
wine			

Look at the words in the box at the bottom of the page. Find the words that rhyme. Use these words to fill in the blanks and make a good sentence. Each sentence will have two or three words that rhyme. Be careful! Some of the words sound the same at the ends, but they are spelled differently.

1. My _____ got _____ in the rain.

2. My mother _____ some _____.

3. _____ has a _____.

4. The coffee and _____ were _____.

5. Pina _____ up _____ _____.

6. She _____ _____ cookies.

7. He _____ a _____ about his _____.

ate	backpack	boat	eight
free	Jack	knits	mitts
note	pet	picks	six
sticks	tea	wet	wrote

1. There's the _____ to the _____ .

2. _____ is _____ .

3. That _____ is _____ .

4. _____ has my _____ ?

5. _____ _____ milk please.

6. Have _____ in the _____ .

7. A _____ and a _____

   by the _____ .

8. A _____ for a _____ .

buy	cane	date	fly
hate	high	I	Jane
Joan	Joe	late	phone
pie	plane	rain	sky
snow	Wayne	Why	

Rhyme Time 6

Look at the words in the box at the bottom of the page. Find the words that rhyme. Use these words to fill in the blanks and make a good sentence. Each sentence will have two or three words that rhyme. Be careful! Some of the words sound the same at the ends, but they are spelled differently.

1. If I see a _____, it will _____ me.

2. He _____ me it was _____.

3. Let's take a _____ around the _____.

4. _____ at _____ _____ at the airport.

5. The _____ on my _____ is _____.

6. There's a _____ in the _____.

7. The _____ will _____ all day.

bear	block	blow	bowl
chin	cold	eight	gate
hole	scare	skin	snow
thin	told	Wait	walk

Look at the pictures. Some pictures are for the **across** words and some are for the **down** words. Each picture has a number beside it. Write the answer on the line beside the picture. Find the number in the crossword puzzle, and then put the letters of the word in the boxes. The answer words are on the clues page. Use them to find an answer or to check your spelling.

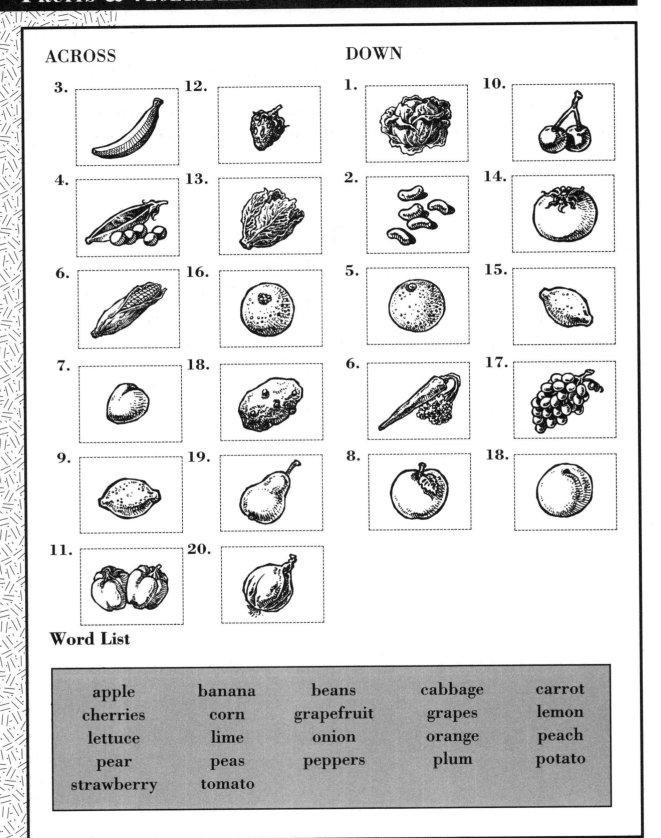

ACROSS

3.

4.

6.

7.

9.

11.

12.

13.

16.

18.

19.

20.

DOWN

1.

2.

5.

6.

8.

10.

14.

15.

17.

18.

Word List

apple	banana	beans	cabbage	carrot
cherries	corn	grapefruit	grapes	lemon
lettuce	lime	onion	orange	peach
pear	peas	peppers	plum	potato
strawberry	tomato			

> The answers to this puzzle are all part of your head. Look at the picture. Write the correct words on the lines beside the picture, and then put the words into the crossword. The answer words are on the clues page. Use them to find an answer or to check your spelling.

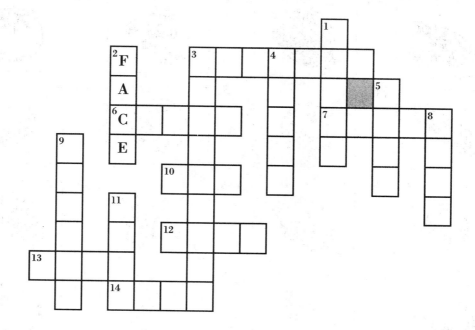

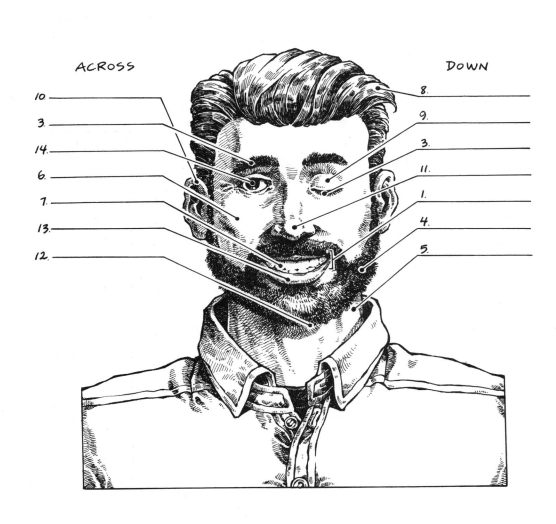

ACROSS

DOWN

10.
3.
14.
6.
7.
13.
12.

8.
9.
3.
11.
1.
4.
5.

Word List

beard	cheek	chin	ear	eyebrow
eyelashes	eyelid	eyes	hair	lips
mouth	neck	nose	teeth	

The answers to this puzzle are all parts of your body. Read each clue and think about the answer. The answer words are on the clues page in alphabetical order. Use this list to help you find the answer or to check your spelling.

ACROSS

3. You have two of these. It rhymes with "lip."
4. An animal on your leg?
7. It lets your leg bend.
9. It's between your shoulder and your hand.
11. They are beside your neck.
12. Stand on these.
13. It goes around your middle.
14. It is not in front!
16. You have five on each hand.
18. It is between your neck and your waist.
20. It's between your hip and your foot.
21. One of ten things on your feet.
22. Black, brown, blond, or white.
23. The back of your foot.

DOWN

1. It shows how you feel.
2. You hold things with them.
3. It's at the top of your body.
5. The singular of feet.
6. The flat part of your hand.
8. You have one on each hand.
10. It holds your head up.
11. Food goes here when you eat.
13. It lets your hand move.
15. It lets your foot move.
17. It lets your arm bend.
19. The large part of your leg.

Word List

ankle	arm	back	calf	chest
elbow	face	feet	fingers	foot
hair	hands	head	heel	hip
knee	leg	neck	palm	shoulders
stomach	thigh	thumb	toe	waist
wrist				

The answers to this puzzle are all parts of a house, inside and outside. If you know your house or apartment, you will find this puzzle easy. The answers are on the clues page in alphabetical order. Use this list to help you find the answer or to check your spelling.

ACROSS

1. You put dishes, pots, and pans in the _____ in your kitchen.
5. Use a _____ to keep people out of your house when you are not home.
7. A _____ protects your house from rain, snow, and heat.
10. You walk on the _____ in your house.
11. You sleep in the _____.
13. Smoke and fumes from your furnace go up the _____.
14. _____ divide the rooms in your house.
15. The bottom floor in your house is the _____.
20. Flowers and vegetables grow in the _____ outside your home.
21. Put your books on a book_____.
23. Look out the _____ to check the weather.
24. Maybe you have a _____ for transportation.
25. If you have a car, put it in your _____.

DOWN

1. Hang your clothes in the _____.
2. You wash yourself and clean your teeth in the _____.
3. Look up in every room and you will see the _____.
4. Open a _____ to enter your home.
6. Cook your meals in the _____.
8. Some people have a _____ where they can make a fire in the winter.
9. A _____ goes around your yard to keep the children safe when they play outside.
12. Go up the _____ to get to the second floor.
16. Watch the _____ to help you learn English at home.
17. Canadian homes have a gas, electric, or oil _____ to keep them warm in the winter.
18. The children play outside in the _____.
19. Look at the _____ on the wall to tell the time.
22. Wash the dishes in the kitchen _____.

Word List

basement	bathroom	bedroom	car	ceiling
chimney	clock	closet	cupboard	door
fence	fireplace	floor	furnace	garage
garden	kitchen	lock	roof	shelf
sink	stairs	TV	walls	window
yard				

To solve this puzzle, think about your school or the people in the school. You will probably find this puzzle easy. The answers are on the clues page in alphabetical order. Use this list to help you find the answer or to check your spelling.

ACROSS

3. There are 26 letters in the English _____.
5. You use this to correct your mistakes.
7. This is what your teachers do for you.
8. Sometimes you will work with a _____ to learn or do something.
10. Your _____ go to school in Canada too.
12. You learn this language at this school.
13. Some people are learning English to get a _____.
17. You learn how to w_____ when you come to school (begins with the letter "w").
18. The teacher writes on this to help you learn English.
21. You also learn to r_____ when you come to school (begins with the letter "r").
22. This person helps you learn English.
23. You learn to s_____ in English classes (begins with the letter "s").

DOWN

1. This word is the same in English and in your language.
2. You come to school to _____ English.
4. Immigrants who come to Canada and learn a new language are very _____.
6. Sometimes you sit at a big _____ with other students.
9. This is one of the first words you learn in English.
10. You sit on this at school.
11. Sometimes you sit at a _____ at school.
14. You can read these things in your language. Soon you will be able to read them in English too.
15. How many _____ are in your class?
16. Immigrants come to Canada from all over the _____.
19. When you come to school you will learn to l_____ in English too (begins with the letter "l").
20. You can write things on paper with this object.

Word List

alphabet	blackboard	books	brave	chair
children	desk	English	eraser	hello
job	learn	listen	name	partner
pencil	read	speak	students	table
teach	teacher	world	write	

The answers to this puzzle are the provinces and territories of Canada. The clue includes the short form, or the abbreviation, and some other information to help you. A maple leaf shows there is a space between words. The answers are on the clues page in alphabetical order. If needed, use this list to help you find the correct answer or to check your spelling.

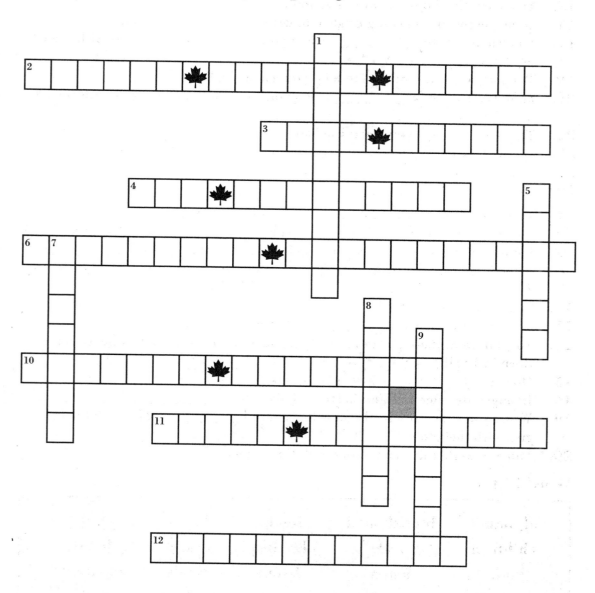

ACROSS

2. P.E.I. ~ Canada's smallest province.
3. N.S. ~ Its name means "New Scotland."
4. N.B. ~ This province is on the east coast, near Que.
6. N.W.T. ~ This is the larger territory in Canada's north.
10. B.C. ~ This province is on the west coast of Canada.
11. Y.T. ~ This is the smaller territory in Canada's north.
12. Sask. ~ This flat, farming province is in the middle of Canada.

DOWN

1. Canada has ten _____ .
5. Que. ~ Canada's French-speaking province.
7. Ont. ~ The capital of Canada is found here.
8. Alta. ~ This western province is just east of B.C.
9. Man. ~ This province is just west of Ont.

Questions

What province is not part of the puzzle? _____

What province do you live in? _____

What is the capital of your province? _____

Which province is west of your province? _____

Which is east of yours? _____

What province would you like to visit? Why? _____

What province would you like to live in? Why? _____

Word List

Alberta	British Columbia	Manitoba
New Brunswick	Northwest Territories	Nova Scotia
Ontario	Prince Edward Island	provinces
Quebec	Saskatchewan	Yukon Territory

Look at the clues. All of the answers are nouns. Each answer is the opposite of the word in the clue. For example, if the clue says "sister" the answer is "brother." The answers are on the clues page in alphabetical order. If needed, you can use this list to help you find the correct answer or to check your spelling.

ACROSS

1. aunt
4. right
6. goodbye
8. east
11. mother
13. beginning
14. brother
15. day
18. no
22. square
24. girl
25. sun
26. man
27. son

DOWN

2. nephew
3. whisper
5. hand
6. feet
7. on
9. autumn
10. cold
12. question
16. wife
17. chest
19. winter
20. north
21. ceiling
23. country

Word List

answer	back	boy	circle	city
daughter	end	father	floor	foot
hands	heat	hello	husband	left
moon	niece	night	off	sister
south	spring	summer	uncle	west
woman	yes	yell		

The answers to this puzzle are all adjectives or adverbs. Each answer is the opposite of the word in the clue. For example, if the clue says "big" the answer might be "small" or "little." The answers are on the clues page in alphabetical order. If needed, you can use this list to help you find the correct answer or to check your spelling.

ACROSS

2. her
4. mother
6. every
7. poor
8. worst
10. narrow
14. sick
15. down
18. sad
21. easy
23. full
24. tame
26. bad
27. boy
29. top

DOWN

1. back
3. tall
5. calm
6. then
9. dull
11. wet
12. sunny
13. loud
16. thick
17. old
19. mean
20. big
22. wrong
25. right
28. bright

Word List

best	bottom	cloudy	difficult	dim
dry	empty	excited	father	front
girl	good	happy	healthy	his
kind	left	no	now	quiet
rich	right	sharp	short	small
thin	up	wide	wild	young

The answers to this puzzle are all verbs. Each answer is the opposite of the word in the clue. For example, if the clue says "sit" the answer is "stand." The answers are on the clues page in alphabetical order. If needed, you can use this list to help you find the correct answer or to check your spelling.

OPPOSITES ~ VERBS

ACROSS

1. end
5. give
6. go
9. buy
10. teach
12. whisper
15. speak
17. fast
20. leave
21. pick up
23. send
24. throw

DOWN

2. emigrate
3. love
4. seek
7. borrow
8. stop
9. sit
11. descend
13. open
14. cry
16. remember
18. leave
19. find
22. pull

Word List

arrive	ascend	begin	catch	close
come	drop	eat	forget	go
hate	hide	immigrate	laugh	learn
lend	listen	lose	push	receive
return	sell	shout	stand	take

The answer to each clue is the irregular past of the verb in the parentheses. For example, if the clue says "(to sit)," the answer is "sat." The answers are on the clues page in alphabetical order. If needed, you can use this list to help you find the correct answer or to check your spelling.

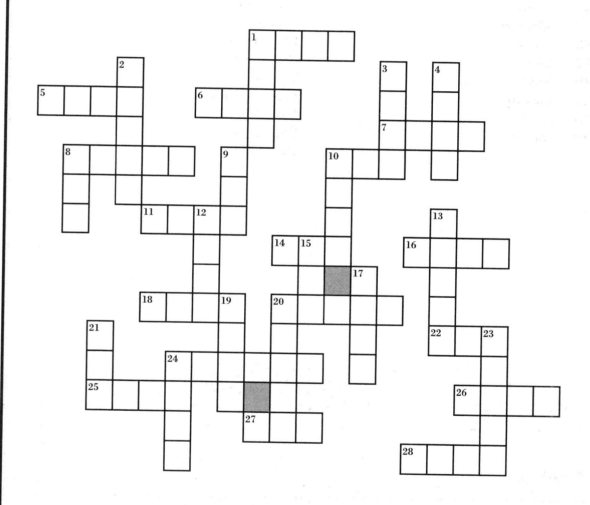

ACROSS

1. We (to sing) "O Canada" last Canada Day.
5. Sim Ying (to shut) the door when the other class was noisy.
6. Ahmed (to tell) us about his family.
7. The teacher (to say) we did well on our test.
8. We (to write) a story about our countries.
10. Anna (to put) her books on her desk.
11. Georges (to hurt) himself when he fell.
14. Maria (to have) a dentist's appointment yesterday.
16. We (to go) on a class trip last week.
18. Mohammad (to know) many English words before he started school.
20. Our classes (to begin) last September.
22. Omar (to do) his homework last night.
24. Sook (to forget) to do the dishes last night.
25. We (to wear) warm clothes when it snowed.
26. The teacher (to make) a cake for the last day of school.
27. We (to meet) many new students on the first day of school.
28. The teacher (to take) our stories home to read them.

DOWN

1. Attila (to sell) his house before he came to Canada.
2. We (to stand) to sing "O Canada."
3. Lula (to lose) her bus tickets.
4. Pedro (to quit) his job last week.
8. Sau Nam (to be) absent yesterday.
9. Nhieu (to cut) her finger this morning.
10. Khowla (to pay) for the tickets.
12. I (to ride) to school on a bus.
13. We (to hear) some funny words today.
15. Fanny (to eat) some eggs for breakfast this morning.
17. Samia (to come) to Canada three years ago.
19. Johanna and her brother (to be) late for school this afternoon.
20. Christina (to break) the glass when she dropped it.
21. Yesterday, we (to see) a movie about Canada's geography.
23. I (to drink) too much coffee today.
24. Michiru (to fall) many times when she learned to skate.

Word List

ate	began	broke	came	cut
did	drank	fell	forgot	had
heard	hurt	knew	lost	made
met	paid	put	quit	rode
said	sang	saw	shut	sold
stood	told	took	was	went
were	wore	wrote		

UP & DOWN GAME BOARD

YOU WIN			go down to 65				YOU ARE CLOSE!		
100	99	98	97	96	95	94	93	92	91
					go down to 66				
81	82	83	84	85	86	87	88	89	90
			go up to 93						
80	79	78	77	76	75	74	73	72	71
61	62	63	64	65	66	67	68	69	70
						go down to 38			
60	59	58	57	56	55	54	53	52	51
			go down to 8						
41	42	43	44	45	46	47	48	49	50
									go up to 73
40	39	38	37	36	35	34	33	32	31
	go up to 47								
21	22	23	24	25	26	27	28	29	30
					go up to 40				
20	19	18	17	16	15	14	13	12	11
						go up to 39			
1	2	3	4	5	6	7	8	9	10

1. child *move 1*	9. meat *move 3*
2. person *move 2*	10. sugar *move 4*
3. goose *move 3*	11. deer *move 5*
4. cow *move 4*	12. half *move 6*
5. fish *move 5*	13. movie *move 1*
6. man *move 6*	14. box *move 2*
7. woman *move 1*	15. calf *move 3*
8. corn *move 2*	16. sheep *move 4*

17. one *move 5*	25. she *move 1*
18. dish *move 6*	26. teacher *move 2*
19. thief *move 1*	27. foot *move 3*
20. cheese *move 2*	28. me *move 4*
21. Governor General *move 3*	29. her *move 5*
22. family *move 4*	30. city *move 6*
23. this *move 5*	31. money *move 1*
24. I *move 6*	32. brush *move 2*

33. province	41. spoon
move 3	*move 5*
34. mouse	42. cherry
move 4	*move 6*
35. he	43. salesperson
move 5	*move 1*
36. tooth	44. fork
move 6	*move 2*
37. toothache	45. knife
move 1	*move 3*
38. snowman	46. couch
move 2	*move 4*
39. him	47. sister-in-law
move 3	*move 5*
40. church	48. brother-in-law
move 4	*move 6*

49. library *move 1*	55. music *move 1*
50. watch *move 2*	56. dictionary *move 2*
51. dirt *move 3*	57. rice *move 3*
52. candy *move 4*	58. milk *move 4*
53. country *move 5*	59. truck driver *move 5*
54. story *move 6*	60. wolf *move 6*

1. Dr.	9. Blvd.
move 1	*move 3*
2. Mr.	10. St.
move 2	*move 4*
3. Mrs.	11. P.E.I.
move 3	*move 5*
4. Ms.	12. Nfld.
move 4	*move 6*
5. P.M.	13. N.B.
move 5	*move 1*
6. M.P.	14. N.S.
move 6	*move 2*
7. Ave.	15. Que.
move 1	*move 3*
8. Cres.	16. Ont.
move 2	*move 4*

17. Man. *move 5*	25. Jan. *move 1*
18. Sask. *move 6*	26. Feb. *move 2*
19. Alta. *move 1*	27. Mar. *move 3*
20. B.C. *move 2*	28. Apr. *move 4*
21. N.W.T. *move 3*	29. Aug. *move 5*
22. Y.T. *move 4*	30. Sept. *move 6*
23. prov. *move 5*	31. Oct. *move 1*
24. yr. *move 6*	32. Nov. *move 2*

33. Dec. *move 3*	41. km *move 5*
34. Mon. *move 4*	42. cm *move 6*
35. Tues. *move 5*	43. mm *move 1*
36. Wed. *move 6*	44. mL *move 2*
37. Thurs. *move 1*	45. L *move 3*
38. Fri. *move 2*	46. tsp. *move 4*
39. Sat. *move 3*	47. tbsp. *move 5*
40. Sun. *move 4*	48. R.S.V.P. *move 6*

49. a.s.a.p	**55. adj.**
move 1	*move 1*
50. TV	**56. adv.**
move 2	*move 2*
51. no.	**57. CBC**
move 3	*move 3*
52. G.S.T.	**58. kg**
move 4	*move 4*
53. U.S.A.	**59. a.m.**
move 5	*move 5*
54. C	**60. p.m.**
move 6	*move 6*

1. I am *move 1*	9. You have *move 3*
2. You are *move 2*	10. He has *move 4*
3. He is *move 3*	11. She has *move 5*
4. She is *move 4*	12. We have *move 6*
5. It is *move 5*	13. They have *move 1*
6. We are *move 6*	14. I will *move 2*
7. They are *move 1*	15. He will *move 3*
8. I have *move 2*	16. She will *move 4*

17. It will *move 5*	**25. It is not** *move 1*
18. We will *move 6*	**26. We are not** *move 2*
19. You will *move 1*	**27. They are not** *move 3*
20. They will *move 2*	**28. I have not** *move 4*
21. I am not *move 3*	**29. You have not** *move 5*
22. You are not *move 4*	**30. He has not** *move 6*
23. He is not *move 5*	**31. She has not** *move 1*
24. She is not *move 6*	**32. It has not** *move 2*

33. We have not

move 3

34. They have not

move 4

35. I will not

move 5

36. You will not

move 6

37. He will not

move 1

38. It will not

move 2

39. She will not

move 3

40. We will not

move 4

41. They will not

move 5

42. I cannot

move 6

43. You cannot

move 1

44. She cannot

move 2

45. He cannot

move 3

46. We cannot

move 4

47. They cannot

move 5

48. I do not

move 6

49. You do not

move 1

52. It does not

move 4

50. He does not

move 2

53. We do not

move 5

51. She does not

move 3

54. They do not

move 6

1. I visited <u>my aunt and uncle</u>.

   move 1

2. We talked about <u>my job</u>.

   move 2

3. Carla went <u>to Ottawa</u>.

   move 3

4. She met <u>an old friend</u>.

   move 4

5. They spoke <u>Polish</u>.

   move 5

6. They went to <u>Parliament Hill</u>.

   move 6

7. Tang Lee had dinner <u>at 8 o'clock</u>.

   move 1

8. I baked <u>an apple pie</u>.

   move 2

9. She cried <u>because she lost her dog</u>.

   move 3

10. We stayed <u>for two weeks</u>.

    move 4

11. We came home <u>by train</u>.

    move 5

12. She ate <u>three</u> hamburgers.

    move 6

13. She left the restaurant <u>at 4 o'clock</u>.

    move 1

14. They took the bus <u>because they didn't have a car</u>.

    move 2

15. Mona wrote a letter <u>to her mother</u>.

    move 3

16. They were in school <u>all morning</u>.

    move 4

17. We did <u>a lot of work</u> at school today.

move 5

18. I sent a postcard to <u>our teacher</u>.

move 6

19. Roni fell asleep <u>in class</u>.

move 1

20. I lost <u>my best gloves</u>.

move 2

21. I had <u>two</u> teachers last year.

move 3

22. We got to school <u>late</u>.

move 4

23. We visited <u>Alberta</u> last summer.

move 5

24. We had a <u>wonderful</u> vacation.

move 6

25. She waited in line <u>for twenty minutes</u>.

move 1

26. <u>My teacher</u> gave it to me.

move 2

27. My sister is <u>in the front row</u>.

move 3

28. I'm cold <u>because I didn't wear a hat and mittens</u>.

move 4

29. I <u>walk</u> to school.

move 5

30. I go to school <u>three days</u> a week.

move 6

31. I finished making my sweater <u>last night</u>.

move 1

32. She took <u>Spanish</u> classes at night.

move 2

33. <u>My brother</u> came to Canada from Hong Kong.

move 3

34. I broke <u>my watch</u>.

move 4

35. They were at school <u>for three hours</u>.

move 5

36. I love Nova Scotia <u>because of the ocean.</u>

move 6

37. <u>Three</u> people were in the car.

move 1

38. We bought <u>a new car</u>.

move 2

39. I sent a letter <u>by airmail</u>.

move 3

40. I want to live <u>in Vancouver</u>.

move 4

41. I came to Canada <u>three years ago</u>.

move 5

42. <u>Our teacher</u> took Spanish classes at night.

move 6

43. We will be in Manitoba <u>for ten days</u>.

move 1

44. He wants to live <u>in a house</u>.

move 2

45. My mother baked a <u>chocolate</u> cake.

move 3

46. She took Spanish classes <u>at night</u>.

move 4

47. We are late <u>because we missed the bus</u>.

move 5

48. I came to Canada <u>by boat</u>.

move 6

49. I love <u>my children</u>.

move 1

55. He's <u>a teller</u> in a bank.

move 1

50. We went <u>to Ontario Place</u>.

move 2

56. Ana sings <u>like an angel</u>.

move 2

51. You can come <u>in the morning</u>.

move 3

57. I have a <u>black</u> cat.

move 3

52. She has <u>two</u> brothers.

move 4

58. I come to school <u>to learn English</u>.

move 4

53. I <u>watched TV</u> last night.

move 5

59. She likes <u>to read</u>.

move 5

54. He works <u>in a bank</u>.

move 6

60. <u>They</u> can speak Russian.

move 6

1. Who/Whom did you visit?
2. What did you talk about?
3. Where did Carla go?
4. Who/Whom did she meet?
5. What language did they speak?
6. Where did they go?
7. When did Tang Lee have dinner?
8. What did you bake?
9. Why did she cry?
10. How long did you stay?
11. How did you come home?
12. How many hamburgers did she eat?
13. When did she leave the restaurant?
14. Why did they take the bus?
15. Who did Mona write a letter to?
    To whom did Mona write a letter?
16. How long were they in school?
17. What did you do at school today?
18. Who did you send a postcard to?
    To whom did you send a postcard?
19. Where did Roni fall asleep?
20. What did you lose?
21. How many teachers did you have last year?
22. When did you get to school?
23. Where did you go (visit) last summer?
24. What kind of vacation did you have?
25. How long did she wait in line?
26. Who gave it to you?
27. Where is your sister?
28. Why are you cold?
29. How do you come to school?
30. How often do you go to school?
31. When did you finish making your sweater?
32. What kind of classes did she take at night?
33. Who came to Canada (from Hong Kong)?
34. What did you break?
35. How long were they at school?
36. Why do you love Nova Scotia?
37. How many people were in the car?
38. What did you buy?

39. How did you send the letter?
40. Where do you want to live?
41. When did you come to Canada?
42. Who took Spanish classes at night?
43. How long will you be in Manitoba?
44. Where does he want to live?
45. What kind of cake did your mother bake?
46. When did she take Spanish classes?
47. Why are you late?
48. How did you come to Canada?
49. Who/Whom do you love?
50. Where did you go?
51. When can I come?
52. How many brothers does she have?
53. What did you do last night?
54. Where does he work?
55. What's his job?
    What does he do in the bank?
56. How does Ana sing?
57. What colour is your cat?
58. Why do you come to school?
59. What does she like to do?
60. Who can speak Russian?

1. OUTLINE MAP OF CANADA SHOWING PROVINCE AND TERRITORY BORDERS, GREAT LAKES AND OTHER LARGE LAKES IN CANADA

2. OUTLINE MAP OF THE WORLD

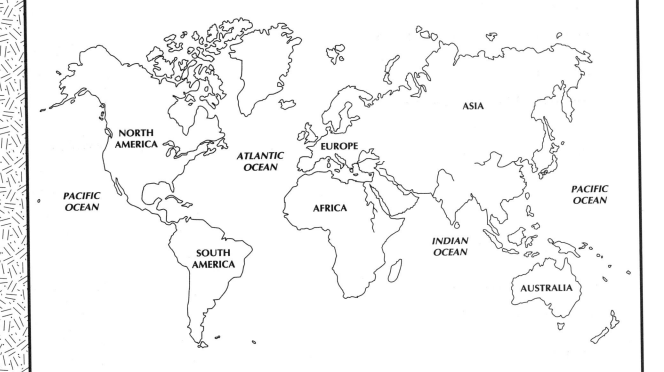

INDEX

VOCABULARY COMPREHENSION

WRITING PRACTICE